# BROTHER ZERO

# BOOKS BY COVELLE NEWCOMB

Running Waters
Black Fire
The Red Hat
The Secret Door
Vagabond in Velvet
Larger than the Sky
The Broken Sword
Silver Saddles
Narizona's Holiday
Cortez the Conqueror
Brother Zero

# BROTHER ZERO

A Story of the Life of Saint John of God

BY

COVELLE

NEWCOMB

With a Foreword by His Eminence Richard Cardinal Cushing,

*Archbishop of Boston*

*Decorations by Addison Burbank*

DODD, MEAD & COMPANY

New York   1959

NIHIL OBSTAT

George A. Denzer, S.T.D.

*Censor Librorum*

IMPRIMATUR

Walter Philip Kellenberg, D.D.

*Bishop of Rockville Centre*

August 31, 1959

To TOMÁS, JULIÁN, ROSALÍA

# FOREWORD

THOSE who work generously and relentlessly for God are often misunderstood and even maligned by their contemporaries. St. John of God, the subject of this interesting story-biography by Covelle Newcomb, was too strong in his personal influence and too spectacular in his actual accomplishment to lose the recognition and praise which so many others fail to gain this side of the grave. Yet the judgment of his own age fell far short of the estimate of his greatness which posterity would form. St. John of God was a man whose vision carried him centuries beyond the time in which his work was done. The methods which he introduced for the care of the sick have become so commonplace that we find it hard to believe that they were not always employed.

A restless youth, preoccupied with the desire to do penance for his sins, St. John of God became interested in the relief of human misery as a means of fulfilling the divine command of loving God in our neighbor. With unerring accuracy and surprising practicality, he sensed the need of far-reaching reforms in the diagnosis and treatment of disease, and he brought down to the level of scientific knowledge many theories regarding the causes of human suffering which had been formulated upon questionable and even superstitious postulates.

Born in Portugal in 1495, young John Ciudad disappeared mysteriously from the home of his devoted parents when he was but nine years of age. After a long and difficult journey he came to Oropesa in Spain, where he fell under the helpful influence of the parish priest. As a young man, he felt the urge to offer himself, as had so many others, as ransom for Christians held captive by the Moors. Yielding, however, to the advice of his confessor, he settled in Gibraltar, where he carried on a work of the apostolate surprisingly modern in its conception and execution: that of the printed page. Printing was still a new invention, but this enterprising young man procured a supply of religious books and traveled around the countryside distributing them in the hope of spreading knowledge about God and His Church.

It was at this time that John received the vision of the Infant Jesus, Who is reported to have given him the name by which he is now known. The turning point of his life was reached as he listened to the sermons of the namesake, Blessed John of Avila, at Granada. He distributed his wealth to the poor and performed acts of penance publicly in the streets of the city. A pilgrimage to the distant shrine of Our Lady of Guadalupe brought him to greater emotional balance and broadened his view of the purposes of the works of mercy.

Returning to Granada, John of God established a hospital, which soon became a model of its kind and attracted the attention of medical authorities throughout Europe. Covelle Newcomb presents in vivid language the account of the growth of John's work and the unusual circumstances in which it was performed. The author's style of writing has been referred to as "novelized biography." In its presentation of essential points, the book is historically accurate; the author adds what she calls backdrops and stage properties without falsifying facts.

Herein lies the charm of the book for readers of all ages. The life of John of God is both instructive and inspiring. For those who have been persuaded that the Catholic Church is backward in its approach to the problems of modern sociology, John of God offers proof of social progress in an age in which sociology as a science had not yet been born. For those who are moved by the example of the great figures of history, the achievements of John of God, as Covelle Newcomb stirringly portrays them, will suggest the inadequacy of any program of social reform which is not rooted and founded in supernatural charity.

Covelle Newcomb's previous works have been well received. Two biographies for young people, *Black Fire* and *The Red Hat,* dealing respectively with Henri Christophe, the slave-king of Haiti, and John Henry Cardinal Newman, won recognition as outstanding books for American children.

*Brother Zero* will appeal to both young and old. I am happy to write this brief foreword for Covelle Newcomb's delightful story of the man whose nickname personified his selfless dedication to the service of God in the poor and suffering. I am happy likewise to have this opportunity to express my admiration and appreciation for the work of the Hospitallers of St. John of God, who after three and one-half centuries have not lost the vision of Christ Crucified which inspired their founder. I pray that *Brother Zero* may bring to a wide circle of readers a better understanding of the significance of St. John of God for the age in which we live.

*Richard Cardinal Cushing*

Archbishop of Boston

# BROTHER ZERO

# ONE

NINE peals of thunder crashed from the bell in the old church tower. Wind lifted the resounding rumble and hum over the roofs of rural Oropesa and up to the castle battlements, where it died away into the quiet night. Alone on a slope, John Ciudad counted off the nine swings of the clapper, then fell to brooding, as shepherds will. Shepherd or no, John would have brooded. Reflectiveness was a dark-hued strand woven into the vivid fabric of his nature. Usually, he loved to hear the deeptoned bell. Tonight, the outflung strokes of sound were as sword blows on his heart.

Why? Perhaps they recalled to him the bells of *Santa Maria do Bispo*, the church of his christening, the church where, until his ninth year, he had attended Mass, recited the Rosary and, at his pious mother's direction, habitually lit a small taper at the Altar of Pardons for sinners most in need of God's mercy. Now a nostalgia had him, a sickness of heart and sense of loss which were not new to him. He had these feelings often. They had battered his heart and conscience for seventeen years. He was nine years of age when he ran away from home; he was twenty-six now. The wound which he had inflicted upon himself by this act had not healed and was never to cease to pain him.

What was he thinking of when he stole from his room in the chill predawn of a dewy morning? Fumbling, as if the

house were not his home but a place unknown to him, he
edged his way out of it, groping with his hands in the
darkness, touching the walls to guide himself and to keep
from bumping into or knocking over something. When
he reached the door that opened onto the *Rua Verde*, he
opened it quietly and quietly closed it. Green Street, like
all the rest in the small Portuguese village of Montemor-o-
Novo, was dead still at this early hour before sunrise. Sky
and earth were misty gray, the dimness faintly pierced,
here and there, by low-burning lamps that glimmered
before images of the Holy Virgin enclosed in glass cases
that stood in hollowed-out niches in walls or over house
doors. The silence was deep, unbroken save for the sound
of his running feet and his hard breathing.

It was ever to seem an impossible thing for him to have
done, an act completely out of harmony with his nature.
An only child, he had lacked neither love nor care nor anything that his modestly well-off parents could give him. A
quiet, self-sufficient child, he enjoyed being and playing
by himself. He was not lonely, not a boy to seek adventure
beyond the gates of Montemor. Nor was there any need
for his parents to be cross and reprimand him, for he was
naturally obedient. Scoldings and punishments which
sometimes provoke a child to rebelliousness and spur him
to run away from home were not within John Ciudad's
experience.

How explain it, then? Human reasoning produced no
answer. It never occurred to John to see it for what it was:
God's strange way of setting him on the long road that was
to take him through thirty-three years of wandering before
he was to find his true work and his cross, the one that was
meant for him from all eternity. His mother, Teresa
Ciudad, saw the hand of God in the odd event of his flight

from home. The fugitive himself caught no glimpse of the Divine Will in this inscrutable design. A humble shepherd in Spain these many years, John pondered it over and over and became increasingly restless. But where this disquietude was to take him he did not know. Certainly he never imagined that his childhood escape from home and country was a painful preparation for the day when, as a layman supervising other laymen, he would lay the foundations of a great religious Order. Such an idea was as immeasurably remote from his thoughts as was the glow of his little fire on the slope from the diamond-blaze of the farthest star.

John's response to the impulse that took him away from home was a response to grace. It was not dissimilar to the urge that caused Saint John Calybites to leave parents, home and fortune, although the circumstances differed. John Calybites was a youth. He vanished alone, having in mind a life of seclusion in a monastery at Gomon on the Bosphorus. Six years later, he returned to the place of his birth, but as a beggar of such emaciated appearance that not even his parents recognized him. Nor was it until he was dying that he made his identity known to his mother. John Ciudad was only a child when this urge overcame him. He never knew why he left home, and he never knew why he disappeared from Portugal in the company of a young man who had begged a night's shelter in the house of Andres and Teresa Ciudad, who were known for their hospitality to strangers. The man introduced himself as a seminarian on his way to Madrid. He offered no further particulars about himself, not even his name. The Ciudads thought nothing of that. In their household, it sufficed to say simply *Senhor* when speaking to a stranger. They never asked questions of those to whom they gave hospitality. Kindness was their object, not information.

When John wondered why the seminarian had let him follow him from Portugal to Spain, instead of sending him straight back to the *Rua Verde*, he knew that, as far as he was concerned, there was as little use in trying to solve this riddle as that of why he left home in the first place. That the seminarian was elected by Providence to participate in this curious drama did not suggest itself to John. At that, the seminarian played his part indifferently. Neither surprised nor pleased to find the boy at his side, he took him along as though it were his duty. John's remorse at having run away, his homesickness, tears and weariness brought sharp words rather than comfort. Except for expressions of annoyance, the seminarian scarcely spoke to John during their long walk of a hundred and twenty miles. At the end of that distance, they came to Oropesa. The Spanish village and its outlying area were owned and controlled by Don Fernando Alvarez de Toledo, the Count of Oropesa. A square-towered castle was his home, and his extensive lands were covered with sheep. The Count owned hundreds and hundreds of sheep and employed many shepherds who were under the supervision of a chief shepherd, or *mayoral*, whose name was Francisco Gonzales. The chief shepherd and his family also were to have major roles in the strange story of the runaway from Portugal, for it was at Oropesa that the seminarian disappeared from the scene. More than gladly he left the bewildered and worn-out John in the care of Francisco Gonzales, and then continued his journey alone.

Having reached the age of twelve, John was given a little flock of his own to watch over, and as time passed, his foster father, Francisco Gonzales, made him the overseer of the estate which the Count of Oropesa had settled on the Gonzales family in recognition of devoted service. As supervisor of the mayoral's farm and flocks, John showed exceptional astuteness. Under his careful eye, Francisco's modest means waxed into a fortune. Seemingly without effort, John did the work of a dozen men and still found time to groom the Count's prize stallions and to tend a flock of sheep.

Now, and not for the first time, John wondered whether this was the life that he wanted. Was he always to be with sheep? He would like to do something for his fellow men. But what? Musing, he fingered a twig, threw it into the fire before which he was sitting cross-legged. He stared at the flames as if to catch an answer in their thin hissing.

All was hushed. His sheep lay about the slope, motionless as stone. How still the night, how dark, except where

the moon poured green-tinged light and other shepherds'
fires sprang up like clumps of poppies newburst into
scarlet bloom. Fires like these would be reddening the
countryside around Montemor-o-Novo, too. Home. Again
he asked himself, as he had a thousand times before:
"What made me do it? My mother. My father. Are they
alive or dead? And my uncle? And the old hermit in his
hut on Mount Occa? The things he imagined! The tales
he made up!"

*John, the bells of Santa Maria do Bispo rang of them-
selves when you were born. The ropes hung slack. No
mortal hand touched them. Yet the bells flew wildly.*

"How he enchanted me! I wanted to stay and be a
hermit with him. He would not have me."

*You'd find it too lonely, John. You would miss the world
and the world would miss you. Besides, if you are to become the glory of Portugal, you will have to work, work,
work, when you grow up.*

"I, the glory of Portugal!" John smiled ruefully. "But of
course he was only talking. He must have said the same
thing to everybody that climbed his summit, for he knew
well enough that all boys dream of being heroes and of
bringing glory to their country."

Looking back, John could understand the hermit saying
that to him, also what he said about unseen angels pulling
the bell ropes at Saint Mary of the Bishop, the Ciudads'
parish church, and about the fiery pillar of celestial light
that suspended itself over the house of Andres and Teresa
Ciudad on the eighth day of March, 1495, the day and
month and year of his, John's, birth. After all, it was to be
expected that a mountain solitary with a reputation for
seeing and reading omens would entertain little boys
with incredible stories, realizing that young children relish

the fabulous. What had brought the hermit back to mind? Oropesa's bell, perhaps. He had forgotten those stories, almost. But not even after seventeen years away from Portugal had he forgotten the way the hermit looked at him when he said he would have to work, work, work for the reward of glory. A face so impassive as to be expressionless, at that moment, John recalled, it wore a look of pity. Thinking aloud, John said: "The marvels he described he is bound to have invented. His gift of prophecy, no. That was real. It told him rightly that a boy who forsakes home and country without a reason is surely to be pitied."

Caught in a web of memories, John neither heard nor saw his foster father, the mayoral. Puffing from his walk up the slope, he was standing not far from the young man, as intent upon the tall, lean shepherd as the shepherd was upon his disturbed thoughts. John's large black eyes were luminously sad, and in the moon's glow his narrow, oval face of a slightly olive-tinted pallor acquired a peculiar vividness which made the mayoral gaze at him with awe. However, the sensible rustic quickly rid himself of the notion that the handsome features emanated a radiance unrelated to the moon's. One had only to look at the sheep to know that moonlight was deluding. They were no longer sheep but mounds of stone with the sheen of pale silver. His glance returned to John, who sat like one hypnotized.

Don Francisco frowned a little, both puzzled and fascinated. What was John staring at? Why that intensely sorrowful expression? As a boy, youth and now a man, John's look was invariably grave. He was not conscious of this, but others were. It was natural to him. Precisely what he, the mayoral, had told his daughter Maria Paz just before he came to fetch John home. Silently, he reviewed his conversation with his daughter. "Outwardly cheerful or not, Maria Paz, that sad look is always in his eyes. He is Portuguese by birth and the Portuguese are tinged with melancholy. So are we. Every Spaniard is carnival and Lent combined. Don't take his moods so much to heart, even though they are as contradictory, one to the other, as the rhythms in a Spanish dance." Say what he would to Maria Paz, he had been unable to console her. The only one who could do that was the strong and gentle giant who sat there and looked skyward, his face bathed in a spectral light. In what was he absorbed? Maria Paz? Don Francisco hardly dared let himself hope for that.

Abruptly, with heavy tread, he moved toward John. If those wide black eyes were asking riddles of the stars, he had a few questions of his own to put to the stargazer. Beside him now, he paused. He wanted to grip John's arm and give him a stiff shake. To his surprise, he could not. In this meditative mood, John was a different man, too strangely unfamiliar to be roused in any save a casual way. Timidly, almost, the mayoral stretched out his hand, hesitated, then patted John's shoulder with the tenderness he would have shown a lamb.

"You, John," he said good-naturedly, "come down to earth, will you?"

John's mouth curved in a slightly dazed smile. Then a thought crossed his mind that made the smile fade. What urgency had taken Don Francisco from his late supper and brought him to the slope? "Señor, why are you here at this hour? Is something wrong? Do you need me?"

"Yes, something's wrong. However, it isn't I who need you but Maria Paz."

"Maria Paz!" John sprang to his feet. "Has she hurt herself? Is she ill? Shall I go for the Count's doctor?"

"Oh, John!" Don Francisco sighed. "Sit down," he said, "sit down." The mayoral gathered his brown cloak about his short, plump figure and seated himself opposite the younger man, near the fire. He laughed a little, half exasperated, half amused. "Why, John?"

"Why what, señor?"

"Why is it that you've but a single thought? Is someone hurt, is someone sick! You ought to be a physician."

With a long and sensitive hand, a hand that was made to soothe and heal, John fanned the coals to a brighter glow and threw more faggots on the fire. "A physician must have knowledge of many things, and the brains to acquire it. I lack the requirements," he said, honestly unaware that his whole towering outward aspect was animated by a rare intelligence. His dark gaze fixed itself on the waving flames, as he added, "So it's as well that I never let myself dream of being anything." Making a circle in the air with his slim forefinger, he said, "That is what I am, señor. Zero. Nothing."

"What nonsense! I don't always understand the things you think and say, but there isn't anything that you can't do, if you take it into your head that you want to do it. Zero! You! At twenty-six! You're alone too much. Brooding has its dangers. It fills you with absurd ideas."

"It fills me with feelings, one feeling in particular." Again John's face was dreaming as he stared down at the flames. "I have the oddest sense," he said quietly, "that something is waiting for me, or I for something. I wish I knew what."

The other was about to change the word "something" to "someone," but he caught the substitute word back. Still, John had given him the opening he wanted. "You wish you knew what," he repeated, eagerly. "Surely you do know." He waited, but saw no sign of comprehension in John's expression, only a disarmingly simple curiosity. "What hinders you, John?"

"Hinders me, señor?"

For a moment, Don Francisco looked away from the inquiring eyes. What a situation! Here was John, too dense to take a hint, full of a feeling that something, he'd no idea what, was waiting for him. Down there in the valley was Maria Paz, truly misnamed Mary Peace these days. She fled at a glance, like a dove before a storm. She burst into tears at a word. Absently, Don Francisco rubbed his chin and reflected how useless it was to think that John would ever come right out and say: "I want to marry Maria Paz." For one thing, he was too shy; for another, he tormented himself by insisting he was nothing, nobody, worthless and unworthy. Nothingness was a mania with him. It blurred his reason and threatened to cloud his future. If he would but let it, the cloud would dissolve in the glow of Maria Paz's single-hearted devotion.

Don Francisco was about to say that he had come in order to have a little talk with John about Maria Paz. Instead, he said, "You're homesick again, and restless."

"Yes, señor, I am."

"Are you—" the mayoral faltered, "are you going back to Portugal?"

"I suppose the thought of home lurks in the mind of every prodigal son," John murmured. "I've thought of little else for seventeen years."

"But you have not acted on the thought because of us," said Don Francisco. "When you were left with us as a child, we tried to think of a way to return you to your parents. There seemed to be no way. We sent many messages with passing travelers who said they were going to

Portugal. They never came this way again. There was never a reply of any kind. As time passed, we became more and more fond of you. I am afraid we did not want to try too hard to send you back."

"Do not blame yourself, señor." John lifted his eyes and looked at the mayoral fully, and all the affection and gratitude he had for his foster father shone in his glance. "You and Doña Isabel took me in as your own son when I was utterly lost. It is my cowardice that has kept me from going back. One part of my mind fears to return, the other part tells me that I ought to go back. I can't count the times I have fully decided to leave Spain, only to be stayed at the last moment by nothing more substantial than a feeling that the time had not yet come. It was a feeling that took me away from home, and other feelings prevent me from returning." John looked away from Don Francisco. He flicked with a stick at a tuft of grass. "Some day the time will have come," he said softly, "and if I cannot hope for pardon, I can at least leave my savings with my parents." He felt rather than saw Don Francisco's dread of that day and was himself wretched, torn between his duty to his parents and to his foster parents.

There was a little silence between them.

John drew in a deep breath, as if a part of the weight on his heart was lightened by the prospect of eventually helping his mother and father. He attempted a smile and said, "You came here with a problem of your own, señor. Something is wrong, you said, and it has to do with Maria Paz. She isn't hurt, she isn't ill. *Vaya,* then what is the difficulty?"

For a long moment Don Francisco regarded John with silent appeal, as though to say: "Don't leave us. Stay here always. The only thing that matters to us is not to lose you.

Doña Isabel and I would be as inconsolable as Maria Paz, who believes beyond a doubt that you are going to marry her." Well, the sooner he voiced these thoughts the better. He straightened and then he said what he had come to say.

Something close to deep shock clouded John's face. Speechless, he gazed at the flames that bent in a sudden gust of wind. Through childhood, he and Maria Paz had enjoyed a happy relationship of foster brother and sister. She was his shadow, always with him. He remembered how he used to carry her across a brook; how, when lost in thought, he forgot about her and strode ahead. She never complained, never called out to him to wait. Smiling to herself, she would plant one small foot, then the other, in his big footprints, as if in that way she kept him with her. If she hurt herself, she ran to him; if a servant scolded her, it was to him she went for comfort. She adored him as a small sister adores a handsome, understanding older brother. That he knew. But he had not known of this. For her to say that she could not go through life without him! He deserved no consideration, much less the love of this girl who was dear to him, though not in the way she hoped she was. Or was she? He lowered his head and bit his lip.

Don Francisco spoke suddenly and accusingly. "To look at you," he said, "one might think I had brought a hangman's noose, not Maria Paz's heart. Under God's heaven, where is the man, except yourself, who would reject it? She has poise enough to be the mistress of a castle. She is generous, yet thrifty. When she speaks, she speaks to the point. Does she babble foolishly? Never. And, save when she has no reason to be, she is quiet as a little flower, and as pretty as one." Don Francisco was plainly offended. "Yet you," he blurted, "you cannot endure the thought

of living out your life with her. Let alone Maria Paz herself, you also spurn the position, lands and money that she
would bring to you."

John felt sick with grief and bewilderment. "That,"
he said, "I could not endure. I do not want position, lands
and money." He drew his hand across his eyes, as though
to pull away the picture of himself as a prosperous land-
owner.

Aghast, Don Francisco's silence was as hard as the rock
he was sitting on. When he spoke again, he was more
puzzled than angry. "Very well, you don't want what I
should like you to have, for I owe you a great deal. You
have made me rich. But Maria Paz," he exclaimed, incredulous, "your attitude toward her I cannot understand.
If just once you were to look outside of yourself, you
might see how exceptional she is, even in her appearance.
Her skin is fair, not the brown of pottery. She is small
and delicate. Nevertheless, that fragile stature conceals an
inner strength. There is Spanish steel in Maria Paz. Unfortunately, it is not hard enough yet to protect her against
heartbreak."

To John, every word the mayoral spoke was a drop of
acid poured into an open wound. "If I were younger—"
he began, then broke off. "After all, señor, she is scarcely
more than a child."

"She is neither a child nor childish. It is you who haven't
matured."

"Nevertheless, señor, the fact remains that I am years
older than Maria Paz."

"What are years to a girl who loves you? This difference
in age is nothing. I am twenty years older than Doña
Isabel. Yet, in some ways she is older than I. You are more
attached to Maria Paz than you know," he said gravely.

"She would give you peace and contentment. And your restlessness would go away." Hopefully, he regarded John, then saw denial of his words, as the younger man looked off into the distance. "Peace and contentment are not intended to be mine, señor," he said simply.

"I wish you'd stop talking nonsense, John."

Still looking at the grasses and sheep that the moonlight was frosting, John said, "Maria Paz could not hold or change me. I am as I am. But I, señor, I would change her. That bright spirit would be darkened by misery." Shifting his glance from moonlit ground to starlit sky, he continued reflectively, "Somewhere there is something for me, if I can find it." As iron to the magnet, John's mind was drawn to a perpetual yearning, though he did not know for what. He only knew that he'd had it always. Again he said, softly, "If I can find it." And then: "Maria Paz is very young. She will find happiness, later."

Not without you, Don Francisco wanted to say. But he did not. Instead, he said: "Don't blame me too much for wanting her happiness and yours. I think I chose the wrong moment for talking to you, and perhaps I was too blunt." Was John listening? No! He was remote, silent, with a look of sad yet firm resolve.

The faggots snapped and crackled. The sheep slept. Down in the valley, a dog was barking. There was not another sound until, suddenly, Don Francisco stirred from his rock and shattered the spell that John was in with a matter-of-fact statement. "I've had no supper," he said, "and I don't have to be told that you have not eaten. Come along."

"Will you excuse me, señor?"

"No, you're going home with me. Paco will sit at your fire while the flock sleeps." Don Francisco let his cloak fall loose about his sturdy figure. He looked around. "There he is. He's halfway up the slope now. Shall we go?"

Though reluctant to leave, John was no less obedient to his foster father now than when he was a boy. He got to his feet. Towering over the mayoral, he gave him his arm, for he sensed a weariness in him. Don Francisco took it gratefully. They went slowly and in silence down the slope to the house in the valley.

# TWO

JOHN—"

"Yes, señor?"

"Regardless of Maria Paz, this is your home. Remember. No matter what happens, our home is yours. Remember that always."

John looked down at the mayoral with gentle solemnity. "I will remember," he assured him. "How could I forget?"

Hope of betrothing Maria Paz to John had dimmed like a sunbeam blotted out by a shadow. But at least, Don Francisco was thinking, we can keep him with us. He forced a smile, lifted the iron ring-knocker and let it fall with a thud on the heavy door.

Not Elena, the stout, waddling servant, but a breeze-swift little vision in grape-green silk opened to them. At the sight of John, a frail pink suffused the ivory face. Her whole slight form seemed aglow.

John stood with head bent to her upraised face, just gazing, smiling with his eyes alone. Was it possible that he had never really looked at her until now? The glossy light-brown hair just missed being gold. How her eyes shone! Green eyes, clear and sparkling, like fern-shaded water running under sunshine. A gold chain about her throat dropped a small cross set with emerald-colored stones on her braided bodice. He touched it. "Is it new?"

16

he asked, and hoped the question would hide his odd confusion.

A soft laugh. "New! I've had it since my twelfth birthday. I wear it all the time." She paused, said wistfully, "It's new to you because you shut your eyes to everything about me."

They were not shut to her now. Their black depth penetrated green, held her entranced. He seemed miles above her. He could not speak or move. Only his eyes moved as they followed her, followed the rustle of her silken skirts that sounded like the swishing of bramble bushes in the wind.

She darted over to her father, who stood hunched in thought. "Have you asked him?" The excited whisper carried to John's ears. In spite of his self-control, he winced as with sudden pain. That whispered question was like a twist of a knife in his heart.

Don Francisco lifted his shoulders, said nothing. He wished desperately that his dependably serene wife would come into the room.

"Father, you didn't forget?" That soft, amused laugh again.

"No, Maria Paz, I did not forget."

She flung her arms about her father's neck. "You did speak to him, then. Tell me, tell me. I know the answer, but I want to hear you say it."

Maria Paz waited. When he remained silent, she knew. His helplessness to speak cruelly enlightened her. She was fully aware how wrong she had been when she stared at John and thought she saw relief pass across his face like a faint light, even though the sadness in his eyes seemed fixed there forever.

For an endless, awful moment the three stood in silence,

each shut off from the other in his own suffering. John, whose sensitive nature could not bear to hurt or see another hurt, knew that it was he who had torn the heart right out of her. And she was such a child, such a lovely child. The spark was in him. If he let himself, he could easily fan it to a flame. But he believed it would harm them both and leave nothing but the ash of disillusionment. Almost furtively, he watched the conflict between her Spanish reserve and her Spanish ardor, between pride and the humiliation of being thrust aside. Dear Lord! She must think she meant no more to him than the clove pinks that were fixed to her bodice like a spray of frilled, spice-scented coral.

His heart beat quickly, as, with head high, she looked at him, not resentfully but as though to ask, Is there nothing that can change your mind? Suddenly she seemed to John everything that he had ever needed and cherished. With Maria Paz he had always felt at ease. Even as a small child, she had seemed to understand his moodiness. If he did not fling her up into the air or perch her on his shoulder, she would climb up on a chair and cling to him like a small white butterfly. How old was she then? Oh, five or six. Foster brother, playmate, plaything. In a sense she had loved him as she loved her toys, her bits of jewelry and the cricket that he captured for her and housed in a tiny cage. She never neglected or forgot her smallest possession. He thought: she can and will forget me. But could he forget her? He doubted that, for however complete the break he made with a part of his life, the cut never entirely healed. The past remained. The memories of those whom he had hurt were as wounded birds forever imprisoned in his mind.

Shaken as much as Maria Paz was by the blow he had

dealt her, he somehow steadied himself and went over to her. The proud head drooped when he closed her limp hands in his and held them fast.

Quietly he said, "Maria Paz, try to understand."

"That I do not matter to you?" Her words were as cold as her hands.

"But you do, you do. It is I who must not matter to you, for I am nothing, absolutely nothing."

Tears clustered in her eyes and stole down her cheeks.

Once able to comfort her with a word, he was beyond that now. Helpless, he looked around for her father, but Don Francisco had left the room. "Poor little one, don't cry." His compassion was warm but not as fiery as the pain her sorrow gave him. "It is not easy, no, it is not easy," he said. "Believe me, Maria Paz, I have my reasons."

She did not ask what they were. He saw no use in telling her now that on a day fourteen years ago, while minding the sheep, he had vowed himself to God. Why? To what end? He did not know. It was so, that was all. "If things could have been different—" His voice broke. "But they are as they are," he resumed after a moment, "and we must accept them."

"Yes," she said dully.

"What you want, what I might want, isn't too important. What matters is what God wants. There always is God to consider."

"Yes," she agreed, as listlessly as before. Yet his words made her desperate. He was a tower of strength, and she leaned against him, as light and weak as a little green leaf. He was silent. Then he cleared his throat. "Maria Paz, you have a brother and a friend in me. We shall always be good friends."

"Yes." She withdrew her hands from his, turned from

him with a breathless little sob and fled.

John had made his choice. Now what? The answer was not long in coming. Bitter though it was, he knew what he must do.

# THREE

THE sun was not yet risen when John stole from his room. There was a fluttering in his chest and in his legs. Unsure of himself, he held on to the cold wrought-iron banister as, carefully, he tiptoed down the short staircase, then along a passage faintly lit by a vigil light that flickered before an image of the Holy Virgin. Head bowed, the smile on her face was wistful and a little pained. Her hands were outstretched, palms upward. His breath catching, John reached out and took hold of them, as though Our Lady were bodily present in the wall niche. "Please," he pleaded, "please understand, and please comfort them." The image was so real to him that, in his self-abasement, he half-expected the hands to withdraw and the head to look away from him. Abruptly, he let go his hold on the delicately carved fingers and hurried to the door. He stopped, looked back. No, there was no one about. The hush was profound. No one, nothing, stirred, only the diminishing dab of flame pulsed weakly, like a tiny golden heart about to cease its beating. The beat of his own heart quickened, drummed in his breast. He slid the bolt, let himself out, then guardedly closed the door behind him.

He paused again, as if unwilling to follow the decision he had meditated the night long. "Am I really leaving, after seventeen years?" He addressed the door as much as himself. Staring at the familiar oak, he seemed to see straight through it into the house, into the faces of the three people he knew and cared for so deeply. "Don't mind too much. I'm not worth the weight of a single tear," he was saying. "I should like to have done what you wished. But how could I? Even if I'd anything to offer Maria Paz, I still could not marry her. I wish you had not taken me in," he cried, out of his own inner misery. "But you did, and you gave me everything worth having. I repay you with betrayal and heartache. May God forgive me. And you, too, if you can." Intently he looked at the door, impulsively put his hand to its smooth surface and caressed it. Dimly aware now of the sun's fire flaring up in the east, he dropped his hand to his side. With swift urgency he strode off, toward the town of Oropesa.

The farther he went the more clear became every detail of the only home he had known these many years. Homeless once more, John wondered if any except the homeless really knew what it meant to have a home. Broken up and aimless as the tattered mist the wind was carrying afar, he walked as in a trance over a countryside as familiar to him as the sun that was burning away the last grayish fragments of night. Yet for John it had become suddenly alien and unreal. The darkish slopes, where for countless days and nights he'd tended sheep, were cloud banks, not gentle rises beginning to be burnished with slow-flowing light. Those white shapes above the castle turrets? Clouds? No. Wild swans flying across a field all flowery blue and rose, with here and there a patch of heliotrope. A rooster crowed. Or was it a castle attendant blasting away on a cracked trumpet?

All at once, the sharp, cold tang of lavender, the warm spice of clove pinks brought him back to reality. If all else seemed without substance, this mingled redolence was painfully real. The scent of lavender stung his heart, the way sleet stings the face; the other perfume burned it. Lavender. Clove pinks. Maria Paz. They were her favorites. She gathered armfuls of the pungent spikes and small carnations, her face a solitary white blossom above her sheaf of pale purple and brilliant coral blooms. He closed his eyes to shut out her face, took longer strides, walking faster and faster, as though to escape not only the haunting fragrance that welled up all around him in the sun's warmth but also a welling sense of guilt.

At last, he reached the village plaza, with the square-towered church facing it. He went up to the doors and pushed them open. Inside, all was dark, save for a palely gold haze of candlelight over the main altar. The priest, the same who had been his tutor as well as confessor, was saying Mass. John dropped to his knees in the shadows near the doors. Pray he could not. He could only picture the dismay of the Gonzales family, for by now Elena surely would have discovered the slipped bolt. For a few minutes he knelt with his palms against his eyes; then, afraid that one or more farm hands might have been sent in pursuit of him, he rose quickly and walked out into the empty plaza, where a light wind made pale green fountains of the spindly, willow-like trees.

He glanced around. There was no one. He could give himself a moment to think what to do next, though only a moment. It wasn't safe to linger in the plaza. No question but that he must go. Yes, but go where? Did it matter? Who cared? He would strike out for Madrid. The capital of Spain was less than a hundred miles distant. How far had the stranger said, exactly? Ninety-three miles from Oropesa, the man in whose company he, John, had left

Portugal, had declared it was. Madrid had been his destination. Involuntarily, John's thoughts wandered to Montemor-o-Novo, to that first flight from his first home. Then, all at once, he was jerked out of Portugal and back to Oropesa by brisk, booted footsteps, perhaps twenty paces behind him. A tremor passed over him. His flesh went prickly with cold. Feigning indifference, he poked at a stone with the toe of his shoe. He fixed his eyes on the sand-colored object. Quite forgetting that his six-feet-six of height marked him a league away, he reasoned that, if he held his head down, it might be easier to keep searching eyes from his face.

The footsteps came closer, closer.

"John!" a voice exclaimed.

John shuddered, as though someone had thrust a dagger in his back. His head came up with a start. Then he was rigid, and, because he could not utter a sound, he was silent.

"John Ciudad! What's wrong with you?"

Now John recognized the voice. He swung around and saw the Count of Oropesa, wearing the black and scarlet uniform of a Spanish military. He stared at his former master with astonishment. The Count, in turn, stared at him, alarmed by his drawn and colorless face.

"I startled you," said the Count, confused.

John smiled faintly. "Yes, Don Fernando. Had I been able to move, I think I would have jumped nearly out of my skin. You are the last man I expected to see."

"Well, I hardly expected to see you, either." The Count paused, noting a nervousness in the young man that he had never before seen. "John, you aren't here to poke at stones, that I know." Don Fernando's tone was balanced between anxiety and surprise. "Something troubles you."

"Yes, Señor *Conde*. I am beside myself with trouble—
and fear," he added. "I am afraid of being found by a
farm hand or a shepherd from—" He broke off, his attention drawn to a sound of tramping feet and drums.

"My regiment," the Count explained. "Peasants, chiefly."
He saw John's glance rove to the narrow street down which
the men were coming, and he saw him start entwining his
fingers. The marchers, it seemed, reminded him of the
need for haste, yet he appeared confused as to where or
which way to go. "Why, John," questioned Don Fernando,
"what is it? What has changed for you?" His voice was
solicitous, kind. "I've known you long. Can you not tell
me?"

"I ought to go quickly," John was saying, more to
himself than in reply to the Count, who suddenly remembered something that enlightened him. "I think I understand." He spoke quietly. "More than once Francisco
Gonzales has confided his hopes to me. Two days ago, he
told me that you'd never take the initiative in this matter.
Rather than wait longer, he was going to have a talk with
you. Did he?"

"Yes, last night. It was no use."

"You refused his offer?"

"I had to." John sighed. "I wish—" he began, then bit
off the rest.

The Count put out a hand and touched his arm sym-
pathetically. "What do you wish?"

"I'm not sure what," John replied doubtfully. "Just
now, to go away. That's all."

"And what will you do?"

"Whatever I can find to do."

"What about your future?"

"My future?" John showed indifference. "If I have one,

it can wait. This can't. Go, I must. It is the only thing to do." He looked straight before him, taken up with his struggling thoughts.

"You think too much about what's over and done, and you are far too sensitive to other people's pain," said the Count with a pitying look. "You think *and* feel, and that's too much. Give yourself a chance." But John was deaf to his words, unresponsive as an image.

The more remote he became, the more closely Don Fernando studied the withdrawn face. The eyes, the most striking feature, were as unforgettable and startling against the pallor of his cheeks as if they had been two large ovals of jet. An altogether haunting face, the Count likened it to that of a carved Gothic saint in a church. However, while John was as lean as he was tall, his physique was magnificently strong, more suggestive of a captain-general than of a saint or a shepherd. His bearing was superbly military, the Count was thinking. So too was his obedience.

"*Hm—mm,*" hummed the Count, nodding his head. "Put a long sword in that long hand," he thought aloud, "and no stroke will fall amiss." Next moment, he was gripping the young man's hard elbow. "John, come away from your thinking for a minute. If," he said, "if you really are going to leave Oropesa—"

"If?" John interrupted, and looked at him for a second with a dazed stare. His tone of voice rather than the word left no room for doubt.

"Well enough." Don Fernando smiled at him. "Then why not come with me? What do you say?"

"I? What should I say?" John still stared. "I don't understand, Señor Conde. Where are you going with your company of rustics? And why?" His questions were as simple as a child's, and the Count answered them as though

he spoke to a child. "To Fontarabia, on the French fron-
tier, in our kingdom of Navarre. The King of France's
men are pouring into Spanish Navarre. You are really
astray about what's going on. Watching the flocks, burying
your nose in some old volume on the art of healing, either
one draws you away into some kingdom of your own.
Francis I could invade every kingdom in Spain and that's
all the notice you'd take!" Don Fernando smiled, both
amused and despairing of this appealingly simple yet
complex young man. Always present in person, in mind he
usually was absent. When he was thinking, time and affairs
ceased to exist for him. On the other hand, give him a task
and he put body and mind to it arduously.

"In other words," John said, "you're off to the war."

The other nodded. "With you at Fontarabia, the enemy
would be an easy prey. Your size, your strength! You could
catch them two and three at a time, and their mounts as
well. Why should you hesitate?" Then he himself hesitated.
"By birth a Portuguese," he continued, "you are not
obliged to take up arms in Spain's defense. If that's what
holds you back, it is your right."

John caught only the echo of his words. He was looking
up and down the almost empty plaza. No one's come, he
was saying to himself—and he was most grateful for that.
Doña Isabel, with her serene good sense, must have told
Don Francisco not to bother about me any more. God be
thanked! Suddenly he turned to the Count. "About how
long will it take to put down this invasion?"

At last! He seemed partial to the idea. "About how long?
Who can say? A year or two, more or less. What matter?
There's honor in it." He stopped short and looked at John
as if he had said the wrong thing. "Have I offended you?
I did not mean to. Heaven knows, you are troubled

enough."

"You gave me no least offense, Señor Conde. But what you said about honor gave me pause. It's true that I am a Spaniard only by chance. Still, I look upon Spain as my country. To give a year or two, or ten, or my life, to it gives me in turn a shred of honor to cling to." For a moment the gloom on his face dispersed, as if a light were passing over it. Then the cloud reappeared.

Familiar with John's reluctance to talk when he had something on his mind, Don Fernando prodded him, patiently. "Say it, John. What is it now?"

"I'd be no help to you or to my comrades in arms. I don't know the first thing about soldiering. Never," the young man said and flushed slightly, as though this admission were a crime, "never have I held a sword in my hand. Even as a child I did not play at fighting with a blunted wooden sword. I think I scarcely played at all. Childhood usually is a straight if short path to happiness. Somehow, I missed the bend that leads to it." He fell silent, thinking that his manhood but mirrored his early years.

"Is that all that bothers you?" encouraged Don Fernando. "You see barriers where there are none. Not a man in the hundred that I scoured the countryside for has ever been a soldier or wielded a sword. Just the same, they and you will hold Fontarabia for Spain as dauntlessly as the Knight of Loyola, singlehanded, held the fortress at Pamplona during a six-hour cannonade. He paid the price for his heroism. A cannon shot splintered one leg. The wound will stay with him. The young Basque nobleman will limp through the rest of his life. In time, it will come to mean less and less to him."

About this Don Francisco was mistaken. It was to mean more and more. But he could be pardoned for not realiz-

ing that the road to sainthood can be traveled with a limp,
for the knight whose example he was holding up to John
was one day to become Saint Ignatius de Loyola. Neither
could he know that the humble shepherd who stood before
and over him, neatly clad in homespun, quite the opposite
of the elegance that characterized Don Iñigo de Loyola's
garb, was to be hurled with shattering violence upon the
very same road, not by cannon fire but by the temper
of a horse captured from the French. Out of injuries were
to come, for each, explosive flashes of spiritual enlightenment that would make the persons they had been like
spectators peering at the persons they were yet to be.

Now, with a courtly gesture, Don Francisco detached
his sword from his baldrick belt and thrust the gilded hilt
toward his former stable groom. "There," he said, smiling,
"take that as a call to arms. All I ask is proof of its use."
He must never have handled a sword, indeed, Don Francisco commented to himself, as he watched John draw the
long blade from its gold-tooled scabbard of scarlet leather.
Wonderingly, he fingered the shining, whip-supple steel,
transfixed with awe.

"Good!" The Count clapped a hand on John's shoulder.
"Now, let us go."

For a mere moment John hung back and looked about
the little plaza as if he sought for someone. Then he strode
along beside the Count. Steadily, silently, he was setting
forth to prove his valor, though little did he know in how
many different ways and places he must prove it over and
over.

John the soldier lived up to Don Fernando's expecta-
tions. Bold and tireless in combat, an exceptional swords-
man, a hand-to-hand fighter who gave no quarter and
fought with the strength of a wrestler, John acquitted

himself with a competence that matched his obedience.
The battle-ground was one thing, the campaign tent
was another. An uncommon man among common men,
John's presence made itself felt. The response to his recti-
tude and piety was more hostile than friendly. Amiable
and shy beneath his look of austerity, his serious manner
discouraged rather than invited the fellow feeling of his
tent companions. His sobriety spoiled their fun, which
consisted chiefly in guzzling cheap wine and brandy and
gambling at cards and dice. John would sit on his cot,
quietly watching. His eyes bored into the others, not with
reproach but longing. Until now, solitude had been his
friend. Suddenly he wanted the companionship of coarse-
grained soldiers. Stifling his hurt at their coldness toward
him, his sighs finally gave way to prayers. But because of
the soldiers' disgust, he began to conceal his rosary in his
hand and he barely more than whispered the *Ave Marias*.

Then on a certain night, one of the number unexpectedly picked up the leather brandy flask, stumbled to his
feet, flung an arm around John in a mock embrace and
dared him, mumbling, "Put away your beads. Praying is
for women. Be a man! Here, drink up!"

John drank. He was accepted. A new devil-may-care attitude replaced the ruefulness of the man who had brooded
on the pain he had caused those who were dear to him.
Temporarily, his grief-laden heart was freed of its burden.
In talk and fiery brandy, his loneliness burned away like
snow before the sun.

John could handle any battle strategy. Off-duty, he
could not handle himself. He needed a stiff jolt to jar him
back to his senses, and he was to get it, on the boulder-
strewn plain of Fontarabia. Camp rations were low, almost depleted. John was ordered to scour the countryside

for provisions. Time was of the essence. There wasn't enough of it to allow him to arm himself or to saddle the white mare which had been taken from the French. The Lieutenant in command singled John out for this errand because he understood horses, he was cold sober, indefatigable, and he could be relied upon to return with food and linen for bandages.

Calmly, John mounted the nervous mare, spurred her flanks with his heels, and they were off, the mare like a white banner flying in the gilded light of early sunset. Always able to master a horse, John soon admitted defeat. This obstinate animal was not to be governed. She went her way, not his, and headed for the French encampment at the extreme opposite end of the unpopulated plain. Appearing to know the trail by instinct, the horse would not be swerved. Angered by John's attempt to bring her under control, she reared suddenly, rising on her hind legs to an erect position that unseated him and flung him against a boulder. In the stillness . . . galloping hoofbeats. Gradually, the sound and the horse receded in the distance.

When John regained consciousness, the horse was gone, the sun was gone, the plain was a vast blur of dark shadow, although the moon's light was spreading. His brain spun. The buzzing, the ache in his head! The fierce pain in his leg! He could not straighten up or stand. Supporting himself against the rock, he looked skyward, bewildered. Coppery-pink reflections of fires in the distance told him that he was dangerously near the enemy camp. Unable to walk, he might easily be taken prisoner. How was he to get away? What was he to do? He did what he'd always done in the past: he cried out to the Blessed Virgin to help him.

Soon a soft footstep hushed his pleading. His heart fluttered. Turning his head, he saw a young woman close by. She wore the multicolored triple skirts, the full-sleeved waist, tight bodice and starched square headdress of a Basque shepherdess. How beautiful she was in the moonlight! He hadn't the faintest inkling as to who she was or where she had come from. Was she real? Obviously, for she was kneeling beside him now, and in the enveloping silence of the plain she laved the blood from his head and face with water which she carried in a small jug. Then, with hands as cool and soothing as balm, she lightly touched his injured leg.

She did not speak.

John could only gaze at her wonderingly, as if at a vision. At last, in a faltering voice he asked, "Señorita, who told you that I needed help?"

"You," she murmured, and continued to minister to his wounds.

"I?" John looked at her through astonished eyes. "I couldn't have. I don't know you." Trying not to peer too intently at the exquisite profile, he mustered the courage to ask a question. "Who are you?" he whispered huskily. "Tell me, who are you?"

She stood. "I am she to whom you called for help. In future, my son, be more faithful in your prayers." Still holding the water jar, she smiled an irresistible smile and vanished.

Now to the anguish of remorse was added that of confusion. It had all seemed quite real at first. No longer was he sure. Had the Mother of God attended him in the guise of a shepherdess of the region? Or was it a true Basque shepherdess who had just happened along with a jug of water? She looked very young. Would so young a woman have called him "my son"? And how could an ordinary shepherdess know that, in deference to human respect, he had exchanged good habits for bad and neglected his prayers? It was hard to give credence to either possibility. He must have imagined it. No, he hadn't. The memory of her beauty, her touch, was vivid. The mild rebuke seared his conscience. These remained. But his pain had disappeared. A baffling recovery, mysterious as the shepherdess who, apparently, had brought it about. The throbbing ache in his head was gone, so was the buzzing. His leg did not hurt. He could stand, he could move, stride, run. His injured body was healed, and his spirit, too. The tumble had shocked him back to his senses. This he knew; but he did not know that the temperamental horse had thrown him headlong into the path of sanctity. Yet even now he was seeing things in a new way, or rather in the way he saw them before he tried to make himself over, after the pattern of other men. What had seemed pleasant, even necessary to him but a few hours ago did not seem so any more. The past he could not undo. But he could try to make reparation for it.

All in an instant, John resumed his former ways and habits. When he was not fighting, he was praying, assisting the camp surgeon, nursing the stricken with a patience and manly tenderness that never failed to encourage and comfort the sick and the wounded. He asked nothing of anyone, he desired neither praise nor rewards.

The months dragged into a year.

Then another year.

Late one night, his commanding officer came to him with a chestful of loot which had been seized from the French. This he entrusted to John, who was to guard it until daybreak. He was not often tired, but this night he was. His efforts to stay awake were futile. The chest was the last thing he saw when sleep overcame him, but not the first thing when he awoke. It wasn't there, nor could he find it. With pounding heart John reported the calamity, never suspecting that the officer himself had crept back to the tent and made off with the box while he was sleeping. Rankled by the quality of goodness which John possessed in the highest degree, and jealous of him, the man had contrived the plot in order to condemn John unjustly. If John's breathing stopped for a moment or so as he stared at the officer, who pronounced the death sentence for him, he did not protest it, although he firmly protested the charge of theft.

While John awaited the day of his hanging, rumors and conjectures circulated about the officer. Some of the men who had ridiculed John's piety now bribed a courier to take a message to the Commander-in-Chief, the Count of Oropesa, who made his headquarters in a village perhaps twenty miles away. The Count replied by arriving in person with an order for John's release. He came not a minute too soon to save John's neck from the noose. As hastily as his deliverer had come, John left, forced to accept his discharge from the regiment. Taking his few belongings with him, he followed Don Fernando's advice and returned to Oropesa and his old occupation of shepherd. There he stayed until the Holy War of Charles V against the Turk, in Austria-Hungary, offered him his second escape from Don Francisco's standing offer of his daughter in marriage. At the war's end, John Ciudad had gold in his purse, medals on his chest and the resolve to go home.

His home-coming was a Calvary, not the joyous occasion he had anticipated. Montemor-o-Novo had changed and grown. Strangers lived in the house on Green Street. They nor anyone else recognized him. Far worse, he could not find his parents or a soul who knew them. It was not until he located his aged uncle, Alfonso Duarte, that he realized there was no use staying. His father and mother were dead. His uncle urged him to make a new life for himself elsewhere, for grief would never let go its hold on him if he remained in Montemor. So John, crushed and bereft, left his savings and his tokens of valor with Alfonso Duarte and sensibly went back to Spain.

Not so sensibly, zeal for martyrdom burned in his mind. This could be had in North Africa, where Christians were captured by the Infidel, sold as slaves and tortured. Or, they were lured into the snare by false promises, in return for which they abandoned their Faith. Gladly, thought John, would he endure the harshest physical abuse and pay with his life, could he but expiate his sins by snatching even one Christian from the hands of the Infidel. Regardless of where he was, North Africa was his goal. But first he must get to Gibraltar.

After almost a year of wandering through southern Spain, taking odd jobs here and there, he worked and walked his way to Gibraltar. Directly across the Strait lay Ceuta, a Portuguese possession on the Barbary Coast. He determined to go to Ceuta. And from there? Did it matter where he went, as long as he could pursue his purpose? Nothing mattered any more, nothing except the relentless need to atone for his sins, and what better way than to save others from the grievous sin of selling their souls to the Moors? John was still too undone by his brief stay in Montemor to care whether he lived or died in the attempt. Yet no sooner had he stepped aboard the boat in Gibraltar than his attention fixed itself upon an impoverished family of Portuguese exiles. The Count da Silva was sickly and ageing. His wife and four daughters were troubled and

frightened. Immediately, John's compassion was kindled.
For the time being, he forgot about the Infidel. A new
impulse brightened his eyes, and a slow smile softened his
grim face.

Ever since the day he ran away from home John had
been wandering through life along a road as vague as the
future. After each successive bend, a crisis passed or a new
course pursued, he looked for its end, hoping that somewhere he would find his place and the work he was born
to do. Could it be that he had come upon it in the need
of six exiled Portuguese?

It could be—but it wasn't. His wanderings were not
over. The road he was destined to travel had not ended
suddenly, or even shortened. He had a way to go yet on
this path that was trackless as the skies.

# FOUR

FATHER Mateo's second-floor study fronted the street. Through its open double-doors that gave onto a small balcony, John could see a pale apricot sky scrawled over with mauve and scarlet. Flame-edged clouds drifted by like tatters of veiling on fire. Restless with waiting for the priest, he left his chair and went out on the timber balcony that overhung the street.

Above the crowns of lolling palm trees, green-painted minarets spired candle-like from the domes of Mohammedan mosques. Higher than the minarets was the promontory known to the ancients as *Abyla*, one of the two Pillars of Hercules. The other, *Calpe*, the Rock of Gibraltar, loomed directly opposite Ceuta. To the north, the waters of the port of Ceuta mirrored the quivering blaze of sunset. At this hour, the mixture of dust and haze that hung stubbornly over Ceuta's ramshackle houses and filled its network of alleys had a dimly gilded luster.

Only at sunrise, at sundown and under the star-domed sky of night was Ceuta's depressing ugliness masked by an interval of beauty. Unlike her near neighbor, Tangier, Ceuta had no Moorish palaces and fountained gardens. Ages old, its history was one of repeated invasions and conquests. In the year 1415, Portugal captured it from the Infidel and used it as a trading post and penal colony. Until she was to lose it to Spain, in 1580, she shipped political

37

exiles and prisoners to this North African possession on
the piratical Barbary Coast. Teeming with Arab beggars,
Berbers from the hills and desert, impoverished Portuguese aristocrats, convicts without hope of release, embittered Moslems and Jews, Ceuta was a very hole of human
misery and wickedness.

John stood gazing and recognizing. Down there on the
isthmus, a slim strip of swampish ground that linked the
mainland with the headland, squatted the hovels of Portuguese exiles, among them the mean dwelling that he shared
with the exiled Count da Silva and his family. Farther up,
was the dismal prison where, every evening, he visited the
prisoners. Farther still, white against the green hillside,
stood the only house of any consequence, the residence of
the Governor. And, from any vantage point at all, one
could always see the hated fortifications.

His attention shifted. Directly beneath the balcony, an
old Arab beggar trained his piercing glance on the tall
*Nazrani,* Christian. "Alms, alms, for the love of Allah!"
he whined in a voice that seemed as ancient as the plaint.
John's smooth brow puckered. Pity he felt and also a
flicker of doubt. To any who begged in the name of Christ
he gave without hesitation. He stared down into the empty
bowl upraised in scrawny hands. "Almsgiving wipes out
sin as water quenches fire," croaked the Arab. Once spoken
by Mohammed, the words burned into John's conscience.
Infidel or not, the Arab was a man, a sick and hungry one.
He opened his purse, found a coin and dropped it into
the bowl.

"Praised be Allah. And blessed be his prophet!"

"Praised be Jesus Christ!" returned John, and watched
the man shuffle along, only to stop short as the crier on a
nearby minaret summoned the Moslems to prayer.

Five times a day John heard this high-keyed call. He was used to it. Now, though, it froze the blood in his veins. His glance touched the beggar. He had spread a small mat on the ground and knelt upon it, facing eastward toward Mecca, the birthplace of Mohammed. Draped in his long burnoose, he looked like a body wrapped in a shroud. Or was he a ghost? No ghost. Nor was the beggar the beggar but Pepe Mora. "My sins," John moaned, "except for my sins, what happened to Pepe would not have come to pass." Little pictures flashed through his brain of the discontented man alongside whom he had worked on the fortifications. John stared at them in panic. Then gleams of hope blazed through his confusion, like sparks smoldering behind smoke. "If only it isn't too late," he was saying aloud. "There is only one way to know. But if Father Mateo disapproves? Oh, but he can't. He musn't." Beads of perspiration glistened on John's brow. He was still looking down into the street. The beggar had moved on. It was the Arab, after all. John gave himself a shake, then returned to his confessor's study.

When Father Mateo opened the door, he saw John in prayer before an image of Saint Anthony. At the sandaled feet a wick burned in a dish of oil. Every lazy puff of wind lengthened the flame and made the shadow of Saint Anthony tremble on the whitewashed wall. John was clasping a crucifix. His head was thrown back, eyes closed, the lashes black as briar thorns against his pallid cheeks.

Too pale, the priest thought, paler and thinner than a week ago. Was he going to extremes in his strivings to expiate his sins? More tense than composed, John's face told the Franciscan that some worry weighed upon him. Father Mateo noticed something else. He frowned. John was wearing a dark blue cotton garment, similar in cut to

the black gowns forced upon the Jews as a mark of in-
feriority. His head was bare. On his bare feet were blue-
black slippers with curled-up toes, the kind the poorest
Moslems wore. The leather was stiff and hard and lacked
the customary red and yellow stitching. What had he done
with his worn but scrupulously clean white shirt, buff
jerkin and breeches? Where were his soft, buckled boots?
Had he given his clothing away, or had he pawned it at
old Hamid's shop, the better to provide delicacies for the
condemned men in the prison?

The monk's broad, kindly face warmed with a touch of
anger. Quietly he closed the door. Not so quietly he
crossed the room and dropped his Book of Hours to the
table with a thud. John did not move. Father Mateo's
anger burned out in a sigh. He went over to the young
man, tapped his shoulder and greeted him with a smile.

John rose at once. "I didn't hear you come in, Father,"
said John apologetically. He colored a little under the
monk's silence and close scrutiny. As though to escape him,
he stepped back, into the shadows.

"That won't help you." Father Mateo laughed softly.
"You can't hide from me any more than Adam could
from the Lord in the Garden of Eden. Sit down. You've
lost weight," he said flatly, as he sank into his own chair.
"Do you ever take a real meal? Ah, well, I know the answer
to that. But I wish you'd explain that sack you're wearing."

John looked down at the cheap cotton of his robe. He
said, "It's more comfortable in this climate than Spanish
wool and linen."

"Comfortable?" Father Mateo raised his graying tufts
of eyebrows at John. "Out with it, John. Comfort, your
own at least, certainly does not explain it."

"Actually, Father, I gave my clothes to a man named

Pepe Mora. We worked together on the fortifications. I
thought that by showing him a small kindness," John
added lamely, "I could prevail upon him to stay here."

"He left, anyway," the priest said, "and now you wish
you had your Christian clothing back. Where, under
Heaven, will you find it? You were asking Saint Anthony's
help?"

"Yes, but not for that." John looked away from the
priest to the glazed brown statue. "What I have lost," he
said, almost inaudibly, "is priceless."

John had something "priceless" to lose? Father Mateo
pondered this in amazement. Why, he owned nothing but
the *gandoura* he was dressed in, a crucifix, rosary and
Bible. Perhaps the Countess da Silva had entrusted some
valuable to him. He knew that, from time to time, she
directed John to pawn or sell another of her jewels, for the
limited funds they were permitted to bring from Portugal
had disappeared with the swiftness of water dropped on
sand.

"Whatever it is that you lost, it's clear enough that
you didn't lose it deliberately. I'm sure the Countess would
sooner lose a piece of jewelry than have you worrying this
way. If you are reluctant to tell her, I will speak for you."
He stopped. Quite suddenly, John was oddly animated.
His eyes shone feverishly in a face drained of color.
Rapidly, he poured out his story.

"It has nothing to do with the Countess or jewels. I
have lost Pepe Mora, who has lost his soul. If I were not
the sinful man that I am, God would have given me the
grace to help him. But I am so wanting in virtue that
nothing I could do or say was any use. Pray, pray, pray, I
told him. Say the Rosary over and over. Go to Our Lady.
She will show herself a mother to you. He would not pray.

I pleaded with him to see you. He refused. His heart had hardened like the pit of a dried-up fruit. I hadn't the fervor to be persuasive. His apostasy is on my soul. I could do nothing, nothing. He came to hate the Faith he was born in, he hated me, hated every Christian who labored on the fortifications, especially the foreman. The man's a brute. The whip in his hand is forever rearing like a snake. Pepe felt its cutting bite repeatedly. I blame the foreman's cruelty, to some extent, though not as much as I blame myself. I couldn't even make him see how trifling are the comforts he believed would be his in exchange for his soul. Now he is one of the heathen. He lives in their village."

Fumbling with the knotted white cord that girt his brown robe, Father Mateo cleared his throat. "You must look at this reasonably, John. God gave us free will. Save or destroy ourselves, the choice is up to us. He has chosen."

"No, no! Pepe doesn't know what he's done to himself, he doesn't understand. I have to help him. God will hold me accountable for his defection."

"Put this man behind you, John." The priest spoke sternly, coldly. "And put away as well those spectres of sins that continue to torment you, even though they've been a thousand times pardoned. Another thing, unless you overcome this dangerous notion that all the evil that drives others into peril is due to your past, you yourself will be imperiled by despair. And that, I need not tell you, is the devil's choicest weapon."

"The village is midway between here and Tangier," John was saying as if to himself. "If I could go at once, yes, I think he might be glad to see me."

"You're going on no such errand. Are you out of your

mind? You'd lose your life in the attempt."

"Would that matter? What's the death of a body compared to eternal loss of a soul?"

"Depression is on you even now," the priest warned. "It's as visible as a cloud's shadow on a mountain. To imagine that you can reach and save your friend is sheer madness. He has cast his lot with the Infidel. The Moors are not fools. They hang around the fortifications, looking for prey. Do you think they don't know that you tried to dissuade him from forsaking his Faith? Do you think they wear those curved daggers for nothing?"

"I know, I know." John was impatient. "But look, Father, were I to go there dressed as a Moor, they would not touch me. They would presume that I, too, had defected."

"What!" Deeply distressed, Father Mateo sprang to his feet. Pacing the floor, his thonged sandals made a light clatter on the tiles. "John, you have zeal for souls," he said, halting in front of the eager young man, "but this proposition is impossible. Moreover, it is wrong. Take care, my son. You want martyrdom. To suffer that for the cause of the Faith is glorious. But martyrdom is never won by deceit."

Father Mateo had given John a shock. He felt suddenly tremulous and stared at the priest, stunned. "I did not think of it as deceit."

"Naturally, you didn't. You are too wrought up to think at all."

"Then let me go as I am. I beg you."

Father Mateo kept a stony silence.

"Please. I will take every precaution to avoid danger."

"No! I'd say no even if you were worldly-wise, which you aren't. However base and worthless men may be, you

see good in them. Judas has successors, as well as Saint
Peter. You couldn't handle a situation like this."

"Missionaries handle them every day," John argued.

"You are not a missionary. You haven't the graces, the
knowledge, the experience this needs. Missionaries know
the pitfalls. Even they are not able to escape them all the
time." He paused; then he said, "I forbid you."

John looked down at the crucifix he still was clutching.
"If I could only make him turn to God," he said sadly.
"That I cannot, tears my heart out."

"Better to tear it out that way than give it to the devil."
Father Mateo's words fell hard and quickly. "He has a
grip on you already, tricking you, under a mantle of
piety. I will pray for your friend—and for you, too." After
a moment he said, "How wrong you are if you think your
one chance to earn martyrdom has been snatched from
you! The ways to win a martyr's crown are countless. If
God demands an awesome price of you for His love, He
will ask it, in His own good time."

John stared unseeing at the floor. The priest regarded
him levelly. "You've been here overlong. This port is the
worst possible place for you. You cannot endure to see
human misery without wanting to relieve it. There's little
else in Ceuta, and no means of giving relief. You have
gleaned experience in some hard schools, John, but none
harder than this one. Army life at its worst isn't comparable. Remain, and the temptation that besets you now
will master you. It is bound to because of your nature.
Let a man throw down the cross that God has given him,
you are the first to take it up. You took the crosses of an
entire family upon yourself when you stepped aboard the
boat at Gibraltar. You saw the ailing Count, his grief-
smitten wife and four daughters. God alone knows why,

but you made yourself responsible for the care and support of that family. Who but you would do it?"

"I cannot picture the man who wouldn't," said John, shrinking from this praise.

"Without recompense? I've yet to meet him."

"Does one ask wages of God?" John looked at Father Mateo, incredulous. "In serving the Count and his family, I hoped to serve God."

"You have. But I still say the average man would have left them to their fate."

"Not if he'd ever been a shepherd and a stable groom. Could he do less for human beings than for sheep and horses?"

"He could and he does," said the priest, and lapsed into silent thought. He marveled at John's charity, at the hidden vigor in that gaunt body. Voluntarily, the young man had attached himself to this exiled family. By ingenuity and resourcefulness, he had made habitable the wretched dwelling to which they were assigned on the isthmus. Whatever was broken he put together again. He cooked, mended, cleaned. During a prolonged period of illness that assailed each of the six members of the family, it was John who cared for them with competence, kindness and unwavering patience. The day the Count's money was used up, John labored as a stevedore on the quay, loading and unloading cargo vessels. When his wages at this work proved insufficient, he eagerly acquiesced to a suggestion that not a man in a million would have listened to. In dire need, the Count proposed that John work on the fortifications and share his salary with him. From that day to this, he had toiled long hours at the grueling business of rock breaking and then hauling rock, all under the sizzling North African sun. And still he found time to look after the house and its tenants in the capacity of a domestic servant. He never missed a morning at Mass or an evening with the prisoners. Yet this man who was a benefactor to many, looked upon himself as nothing.

"John—" Father Mateo looked up from his musing—"you did well to confide this matter to me. Should you again feel the devil tempting you with a pleasing or heroic opportunity, go always to the priest. Fall toward God, not toward Satan. Now—" He leaned toward his companion, fixed him with his straightforward eyes. "Now, I want you to leave Ceuta."

Another shock. "Leave? How can I? What will become of the Count?"

"Happily, John, you needn't worry about him. He is being recalled to Portugal. His estate has been restored to him. The King's decree is in the Governor's hands this minute, unless His Excellency has had it delivered to the Count."

For the first time, John smiled. "With you, Father, no two minutes are alike. Nothing so tiresome as knowing what to expect. That is wonderful news, about the Count." He reflected a moment. "Had you a hand in it?"

"Both hands. Such influence as I have, I exerted to that end. Yes."

"The Count knew, all this time?"

Father Mateo read John's thought. "He knew. But I asked him to keep it to himself until after I'd had a chance to talk with you."

"Why? It has nothing to do with me."

"Oh, it has. More than you think. The Count is profoundly grateful to you, John. He is anxious to repay you."

"I don't want payment."

"Don't be too sure. It isn't money alone that he offers,

but a home with him in Portugal. His home is a castle. It crowns one of the many mountains of the *Serra de Cintra*. You, John, would be waited on, for a change. Think it over." He watched the young man with a curiously searching gaze.

John thought. His head felt as light as if he already were in the rarefied air of the pine-scented Cintra mountains. He had no one, as he had discovered upon his return to Montemor-o-Novo, no home, no roots anywhere. The sickly Count depended upon him for everything. To himself he said, "I could make myself useful. I could manage his estate and see to all the details that he hasn't the strength to take care of himself. A faint color touched his cheeks. It was the only indication of the pleasure the prospect gave him. But it paled away suddenly, as he recalled Father Mateo's words: *Should you ever feel the devil tempting you with a pleasing or heroic opportunity.* . . . This was pleasing, too pleasing. His eyes, as he looked up at the priest, were calm and still as dark well water. In contrast, there was an almost sharp urgency in his voice. "It is excessively kind of the Count," he said, "but I cannot go to Cintra."

Hoping for this reply, Father Mateo relaxed in relief. "Good, John, good! Then you will do as I say. Go back to Spain. Tomorrow. Take the morning boat to Gibraltar."

His docile self again, John knew from long experience that it was not for him to act as he wished, but as God wished, and God spoke to him through His priests. He looked his gratitude at Father Mateo and gave him that rare smile that seemed to spread light as it softened the sombre expression of his handsome face.

"No doubts, no questions, John?"

"Only this, Father. What will I do in Spain?" Plainer

than his words was the thought he did not speak. His place, his work, henceforth must be in some spot of solitude, or among men, not among cattle and horses.

"What will you do? I don't know. By one means or another, you will discover what to do and where to settle down. God will use you, rest assured of that. How? He alone knows that, and He never makes a mistake."

# FIVE

"TRINKETS four doors to your left." The thin treble voice came from the rear of a murky bookshop. The two burly fellows at whom it was directed made no move. As if they felt the atmosphere of the shop too alien to venture into it, they stood awkwardly on the threshold, Gibraltar's blazing sunshine at their backs.

Don Felipe, the bookdealer, removed his square-lensed spectacles from his nose and placed them on his open copy of the *Sentences* of Peter Lombard. For a long moment he trained his farsighted gaze on the pair. Sticking as close together as dates, they were the same deep brown color as dates. Dark enough to be Moors, thought Don Felipe, and took a harder look. No, Moors they were not. They wore the baggy trousers of diagonally striped red and yellow sailcloth, the dark blue shirts of the same cloth, the sleeveless leather jerkins and the scarlet stocking caps that identified them as Spanish seamen. From the right earlobe of the taller of the two dangled a twinkling hoop of gold.

Able to spot a booklover at once, Don Felipe sighed his disappointment. Whatever it was they wanted, it wouldn't be a book, certainly not Lombard's *Sentences,* a collection of writings from the Church Fathers that dealt with learned arguments on theological matters. The request for a light novel, even, seemed too much to hope for. He knew sailors. They emptied their purses on baubles, ribbons, painted fans and Angel Water, a perfume of such strength that one seemed to see as well as smell it. Trifles they took home to their womenfolk, not books. The fact affronted the old scholar. Indignant, he piped out again, "I told you, four doors to your left. Castro carries trinkets and fancy articles." About to return his glasses to his nose, he set them down, as he heard one of the sailors saying, "We don't want trinkets." It was the redhead who had spoken. Now he elbowed his companion and together they entered the dusky shop.

Happily amazed, Don Felipe rose from his low stool and shuffled toward them. "Your pardon, señor *marinero*," he said to the one with hair and beard as red as Charles V's. "I misunderstood." Eager to serve, he asked, "Had you a particular book in mind? I have all kinds, some old, some new, some nearly new."

Tongue-tied, they stared at him.

"Would you like to browse around? You are welcome." The invitation seemed to leave them senseless. Wanting to be helpful, Don Felipe suggested *The Book of Marco Polo* and Ptolemy's *Almagest*. The Venetian traveler's adventures in Asia and Ptolemy's astronomical findings, it struck him, ought to interest sailors. But a discreet glance at these sailors refuted his logic. He could see that they were hard put to it to name a title. "Perhaps," he said, "you prefer romances. I have just the one, a romance of true merit. *Concerning Two Lovers*, by Aeneas Sylvius." Still those blank expressions! Tactfully he added, "Undoubtedly the author is better known to you as Pope Pius II. One moment, I will find a copy for you."

The redhead did not care who wrote it. He couldn't read in any case. He took a step forward, thinking to stop

Don Felipe, but was jerked back by his friend. They looked at one another and shrugged, then watched while the bookdealer searched for the Pope's novel among stacks of reading matter neatly piled on a wobbly table. Oddly fascinated, they tried to follow his muttered Spanish. "*Hmm,* that's strange," he was saying, "only last night I topped this stack with a copy. Now where would it have got to? And where are *Amadis of Gaul* and the comedies of Terence? What are these? Dull exercises in piety that nobody wants. So! He changed them around again! Under my very nose! But when? No matter, no matter. What does matter is that he hides romances, tales of chivalry and comedies way down underneath these ponderous spiritual treatises. Who does he think wants them? He doesn't think, there's the trouble with him. The next time I see him, I'm having it out with him." Fingering the books impatiently, Don Felipe sent a few toppling to the floor. He picked them up, one by one, and, one by one, he slammed them on the table. "Ah, well, I suppose I should be thankful that he buys them off me, though how he sells these slow-reading cures for lax souls is beyond me." For another few moments he hunted the novel, unmindful of the sailors, who followed his mumblings and shiftings about with their mouths hanging open.

"Sylvius, Sylvius—at last! Buried at the very bottom!" Carefully, he withdrew the book, blew on it out of habit. No dust. He drew a bony finger across the cover, examined his fingertip. Not a particle of dust. A swift look at the orderly heaps of devotional treatises told him that all were dusted. "Dusting and sweeping," he complained, "always dusting and sweeping. He'd do me a greater favor by leaving the books the way I want them left." Taking the book he had found to the sailors, he apologized for having made them wait.

"Oh, that's all right," said Pablo. "We owe you an apology. We let you go to a lot of trouble for nothing."

His earlier suspicions confirmed, Don Felipe scowled. "You didn't want a book in the first place?"

"What good's a book if you don't know how to read?" With a kind of pride, the redhead reminded him that he, Pablo, and his shipmate Diego, were sailors, not shore-bound bookworms.

"Hardly a thing to brag about," snapped back Don Felipe. "If the sailor from Genoa had not been an avid reader, he would never have discovered America." Irritated, he tossed the book to the nearest table, then sharply cut through the silence with a question. "You don't want trinkets, you don't want books. Vaya, why are you wasting my time? What *do* you want?"

"A man," said Pablo. "He saved the lives of all aboard on a sail from Ceuta to Gibraltar. Until today, we've had no chance to track him down. We want to thank him."

"Thank him, then." Don Felipe was snappish. "Why come here?"

"Because, señor, an officer on the mole told us he works for you. He couldn't tell us his name, but he recognized him by Diego's description." Pablo pulled at the big gold ring in his ear. He seemed perplexed. "Several times during the worst of that voyage," he said, "he called himself *Cero*. An odd name, if it is his name."

"*Zero?*" asked Don Felipe.

"Aye, señor, Zero."

Don Felipe wrinkled his forehead.

Thinking that he did not understand, Pablo said, "Zero, like this ring in my ear, the circle that stands for naught, nothing."

"I know what zero means." The bookdealer felt stung, and his voice carried a sting.

"Well, señor, over and over this Zero said, 'I am nothing. I am less than nothing, less than the waves, less than the fishes in the sea. *Cero, cero, cero!*' "

Don Felipe lifted indifferent shoulders. "I've no idea who you mean."

"You must," insisted Diego. "The guard on the pier said we'd find him here."

"Vaya, so he said, so he said. Is he here? Besides, I employ no one."

But Diego was not dismayed. "He's tall as a mast, señor. And thin. Look at him and you say to yourself—he has no weight, no strength. Ha! Grapple with him! He's as resistant and hard as a slab of rock. A big-eyed face. All eyes. Black as night. Black hair, much darker than mine. He wears it cropped short. It fits close to his head, like a cap. Except for the way he was dressed, he could have passed for a Spanish grandee."

"Wait a minute!" Don Felipe showed unexpected interest. "You say—'except for the way he was dressed.' By that do you mean poorly or strangely?"

"Both, señor. He had on a Moorish gandoura, dark blue. Cheap cotton."

"It must be John," muttered Don Felipe.

"John's his name? Then you do know him?"

"Yes. There is only one man in Gibraltar who fits your description. John Ciudad. However, after he saved a bit of money—he worked as a stevedore when he first came to Gibraltar—he bought himself a decent outfit. Some beggar is wearing that gandoura now. I don't think he would have bothered with new clothes if his confessor had allowed him to retire to the desert as a hermit. John's inclined to

queer ideas—not that wanting to be a hermit is queer, if
you like solitude. He does. There are other things—" Don
Felipe took a quick look round his shop. "For instance,"
he continued, "he's a fanatic for cleanliness. And he works
fanatically. Not at all like a Spaniard in that respect. Most
of us have a strong distaste for work. That makes no difference to John. Everybody, he says, ought to be engaged in
some useful work. When he couldn't be a hermit, he set
himself up in business. That's how I happen to know him.
He buys books from me. First he reads, then he sells them,
and when he doesn't sell, which is more often than not,
he gives them away."

"Has he a shop in Gibraltar?" asked Pablo.

"No. I tried to sell him mine. He doesn't want to be
tied down or own anything. He's a street peddler. Built
himself a barrow which he fills with books and religious
articles. Often, in the evenings, he comes here to read—
spiritual works, medical treatises, that sort of thing."

The books that John fed on were of no more interest
to Pablo than lost languages. "Can you tell us where he
lives?" he asked Don Felipe.

"Oh, in the poor quarter, I expect. Precisely where, I
wouldn't know."

"Have you any idea where he is now?"

"None. He pushes his barrow from end to end of this
whole northwest corner of the Rock. He isn't in a given
spot at a given time. Off and on during the day, he slips
into the cathedral, then he wanders to some corner and
delivers short sermons."

"He's a preacher?" Pablo gulped, looking from Don
Felipe to Diego and back again.

"More preacher than peddler, I imagine. Even when
he makes a sale, he immediately gives the money to some-

one poorer than himself. It's possible," he said, after a
moment's reflection, "that you'd find him in an alley, surrounded by a swarm of waifs. Guttersnipes, yet he wastes
hours with them; teaches them their prayers and catechism, hands out colored holy cards and rosaries by the
dozens. I've warned him. Sell, I say, don't give. Stop pam-
pering urchins and beggars, shake off the good-for-nothings
that trail your steps, and then decent folk will patronize
you. All the help that is! He just smiles, a strange smile,
as if he pitied me. He's the one to be pitied. He doesn't
know he has a brain. He thinks only with his heart." Don
Felipe lowered his gaze for a second, pondering. Suddenly,
he looked up, slapped his hand to his brow. "I forgot, quite
forgot. Today is Friday, isn't it?"

Yes, it was Friday. The sailors nodded, the red tassels
on their caps swinging in unison.

"Let me look—" Don Felipe scuttled to the door,
glanced behind it. "His barrow is here. Imagine! He
brought his barrow, dusted the books, then went his way,
and I didn't see or hear him. Comes and goes with as little
sound as a shadow. Unfortunately," he said to the sailors,
"you chose the wrong day. On Wednesdays and Fridays,
he crosses the isthmus to the mainland, to peddle his wares
in the neighboring villages. He's apt to go as far as Al-
geciras, or farther yet to Tarifa. When he makes these
trips, he leaves his barrow here and carries a pack on his
back. It's too bad you came on a Friday. However, he's
usually back by sundown and he always comes to my shop.
If you could return this evening—"

"We can't. We sail in two hours."

"I'll be glad to give him a message for you."

Pablo slanted a look at Diego. "Shall we?"

"Why not? A message is better than nothing."

"What'll we say?"

"You ask me?"

"Of course I ask you. Isn't it your concern as much as mine?"

"It is, and if I saw him face to face, I would know what to say. But to think up a message, that's different."

Don Felipe smiled a little. "Permit me, señores." With a sweep of his hand, he motioned to his reading table at the back. "Come with me. I will take down your words, otherwise I might forget them, as I almost forgot that John isn't here today."

Flanking him when he seated himself, the pair watched him pinch his spectacles in place on the bridge of his beaked nose; they watched him sit patiently, paper in front of him, the quill in his hand hovering over the rim of the inkpot.

"Nothing comes, señores?"

Pablo opened his mouth. Not a word came out. This was far from simple, he was thinking, while he rubbed his weathered cheek with the flat of his hand. He cleared his throat. "Esteemed Sir," he began, stopped. Then: "We thank you for saving our lives. If ever we can be of service to your esteemed person—" He wagged his head. "That's no good!"

"I agree," Diego said.

"Find the words in your own brain, then."

Diego tried. "Esteemed Sir and Deliverer— The ship's master and crew are forever in your debt—"

There was silence.

"And—?" prodded Don Felipe.

"And?" Diego echoed blankly.

"Yes, señor. *And*—what?"

"Oh, I see, I see." Diego beamed. "And Pablo Gomez

and Diego Leon," he went on, "your servants who kiss your hand, give thanks to God and the Most Holy Virgin—" He paused to peer wonderingly at the elegant handwriting and to listen to the tiny fiddle scraping of the quill.

"Give thanks—" repeated Don Felipe, "for—?"

"Not 'for,' " Diego corrected, "*that.*" He waited, then finished the sentence, saying, "That we did not throw you over the side."

"What?" Don Felipe pushed back his stool and stared up at him. "Did you say—throw?"

"Aye, señor, throw. Over the side. Into the sea." He demonstrated with a wide, flinging gesture.

The quill fell from Don Felipe's fingers. "Saints in Heaven! You are wicked, dangerous men!"

"You don't understand, señor. It was his idea, not ours."

"*His?* John asked you to throw him into the sea? You expect me to believe that?" Don Felipe was outraged.

"Believe it or not, as you please. It is the truth," said Pablo, defending his friend. "Did Zero never mention the storm to you?"

"No, never. I recall something about a storm, but what I heard I didn't hear from him." Don Felipe lowered the hinged lid on the inkpot. "I gave it no particular attention," he said, "and I didn't know that John was in it."

"Well, he was, and if he hadn't been, we'd not be here to tell of it. Squalls are common in the Strait. That was no squall. It was a tempest. And no sign of it until it was upon us. It caught us midway between Ceuta and Gibraltar. In a flash, the sky darkened, the wind rose to gale force, the waves struck us smashing blows, the deck sloped like the roof of a house. The passengers were sliding, tumbling, screaming in panic. We got them below, all except the giant, Zero. He wouldn't go. Walls of water swept over him. But water nor wind ripped him from the rail. Then, in the midst of the tumult, he called out, 'Throw me in! Throw me in and save yourselves. I have offended God. My sins have brought you to this peril. I am nothing, nothing. Throw me in!' "

Unconvinced, Don Felipe glared at Pablo. "Why didn't he throw himself in, if that was what he wanted? Why should he need your assistance?"

"We don't know why. But it is the truth, every word of it. We tried to drag him from the rail. Useless. The strength of ten men was in him. We're husky, yet he flung us off with a flick of his hand. And all the while he kept crying out that the storm was a reproach to him from God, and that if he sacrificed himself, God might be appeased and spare the rest of us."

"That is not in the least like John. He is the serenest of men."

"Maybe so, señor, but he wasn't serene then. He was frantic. Not afraid for himself, only for the others." Pablo drew his square hand across his face and shook his head. "There was a lot that we didn't understand. It was all we could do to stay on our feet. He never lost his balance. Most of the time he stood with his arms outstretched to the skies, a crucifix in his hand. He stood there that way, even when the deck dipped to the sea. After a lull, he would begin again, shouting to us that the sooner we got rid of him, the sooner the storm would abate."

"Assuming that you're telling the truth," said Don Felipe, "how could you let yourselves be swayed by his ravings?"

Diego answered simply, "We were afraid. There was something about him— We began to think that perhaps God was asking this sacrifice of him. The wind caught his

voice and cast it back at us. 'Throw me in! It is your duty
to the souls in your care.' Then, too, señor, the waves
became higher and heavier, the wind more furious. The
vessel shook and groaned. We were sure it was only a
matter of minutes before she'd capsize, so we reasoned
what difference whether we did as he demanded or let him
sink with the ship."

The old bookdealer followed this account openmouthed
in horror. Yet, in spite of himself, he asked, "And then
what happened?"

"We staggered over to him and lifted him off his feet."
Diego paused. "That was another funny thing. When we
struggled to get him below deck, we couldn't budge him,
but when we yielded to his pleadings, he seemed to weigh
no more than the froth that churned around us. Just as
we were about to swing him over the side, he roared out,
'Lord, save us, for we perish!' He kissed his crucifix and
then, in the same big voice, prayed the *Ave Maria*. On the
Amen, it happened. Like that! The gale slowed to a
breeze, the battering waves receded, the sea flattened like
a pricked bubble. The clouds broke, showing the sun."

Don Felipe said nothing, but Pablo knew that he was
thinking, What a sea story! "Ask the ship's master, ask
anybody who was aboard," he defied him. "Diego and I
were too dazed to move. Other sailors were running about,
the master thundered orders, passengers wept and laughed
in one, and everybody was crying out, 'Miracle! Miracle!'
And believe me, señor, it was a bad moment for us when
we recovered our wits. Our arms were hanging at our
sides. Neither of us was sure whether we had or hadn't
tossed him into the sea. Then one of the crew told us that
Zero had hurried below and concealed himself in a cabin.
We hadn't words for our relief. We just cut the sign of

the cross on ourselves."

Don Felipe had no words either. He folded the message, walked to the barrow and dropped it in. He stood a moment looking at the book cart, then looked at the dusted books, the hidden novels. "You haven't seen him since that day?" he asked the two who had followed him to the front of the shop.

"No, señor."

"I'll tell you what," he said, "name a day that you can come, and I'll see to it that John is here."

"Monday next," Pablo told him.

"Good! I'll ask him to clean the shop. That will keep him here."

"A thousand thanks, señor."

"My pleasure." Don Felipe spoke formally, yet with a certain mellowness to his voice that was new.

"Until Monday, then." Pablo nodded. Diego nodded.

But neither Don Felipe nor the sailors had any way of knowing that the appointment already had been made too late.

# SIX

CACTUS clumps, the blue-tinged green of aloes and twists of violet-crimson fire that were crooked trunks of cork oaks, peeled of bark, relieved the tawny monotony of the arid seacoast plain. Heat brooded over the shadeless waste, and all was silent as the mute, white-blazing sky above it. Not a sound. No faintest breath of wind to rustle the brittle herbage. Nothing stirred—nothing except a long, slow-moving shadow. Only—the shadow was not a shadow but a lean giant who was dressed in black-trimmed umber. Over his right shoulder was slung a pack sack which seemed to bear down on him as though it were filled with rock. He plodded as if through heavy sands, not shallow dust, and, from time to time, he swayed unsteadily.

Normally, John was swift and buoyant as flame; normally, he gave off an aura of flamelike vigor. Now? Now the man of great endurance felt a sickish weakness in him. His face was sallow with fatigue. Gone was the luster from his eyes; gone, too, the erect, relaxed bearing, the easy stride that recalled the soldier. He leaned slightly to one side and bore himself stiffly, as though he suffered from a wound in his shoulder and wounds, as well, in his feet. He limped noticeably. The soaring flames of his energy and power of will appeared to have died out. Do what he would to pit his resoluteness against his languor, he lagged

and drooped, scarcely able to stay on his feet. The times
he had spanned this yellow emptiness with a speed that
magically reduced it! Today, the same trail stretched away
endlessly.

Why? Baffled, he sought a reason for the lassitude that
bound him as with ropes, so that he could barely move.
Why was he weak as a cut vine stem? Why the rapid heart,
the din in his head as of hammer blows on anvils? Was
it the sun's burning heat? How could it be? For years, for
most of his life, he had walked and worked out under the
sun, as indifferent to its fiery rays as to the moon's cool
glimmer. If that was the answer, why had it not affected
him earlier, even as it seemed to have affected the people
in the villages he had passed through? Never had he found
streets and plazas as empty as today. Folk stayed indoors,
in well-shuttered rooms. When was he first aware of this?
It was immediately after he left the wayside chapel where
he had spent the noon hour in contemplation of the
solitary image that reigned there: a painted wood figure
of Christ at the Pillar.

How could that have anything to do with it? He doubted
that it had. But there was no doubt about the impulse
that seized him just as he was about to head northward,
back to Gibraltar. As firmly as a hand on his shoulder, it
turned him in the opposite direction. To what purpose?
He did not know. He'd no clear idea, even, as to where he
was going. As far as his blistered feet would carry him?
Tarifa? And if he reached it, what should he do there?
Roam empty streets, as he had roamed them all morning?
People twenty miles back were too wilted with the heat
to accept—he didn't ask them to buy—rosaries and copies
of *The Imitation of Christ*. Could he expect more enthusiasm in Tarifa? Only a few had bothered to peer at

him through the door wicket, and they had peered as at a half-wit who was to be refused and smirked at.

Discouragement deepened in him. If his sack was as heavy as when he left Don Felipe's shop, unnoticed, it was his fault, no other's. Could he deny that his mind was not on his job but on his early return to the soothingly dark bookshop? No wonder he spent the day to no profit. No wonder he lacked persuasiveness, when he had no thought except to lose himself in the shadows, with a book, or just doing nothing. Were it possible, he would retrace his steps, starting this minute, and try harder to rouse the sluggish to greater fervor for the cross. But retreat was out of the question. With every breath he would say: I can't go on, I can't. Yet he knew that he must.

The unseen hand on his shoulder, the soundless voice

that commanded him were not to be ignored. He had long acquaintance with these urges and obeyed them as he obeyed his confessors. What was to come of this one he could not imagine. Small good he was to anyone, without strength, without will power. Of the latter he hadn't enough to resist the desire to make himself comfortable. Precisely when he had allowed himself to yield to this temptation, he was not certain. But that he had was certain, and disturbing. His shirt lay open at the neck. His burnt-umber doublet hung open, and the side fastenings, just below the knees, on his full, unpadded canions, were open, too. His legs were bare. Somewhere in this simmering region he had stopped to pull off his scratchy wool-knit stockings. Vaguely, he recalled that he threw them to the ground, only too glad to be rid of them. Quite unlike himself, he had not troubled to slip the black buttons on the flaps of his knee breeches through the loops that served to hold them. His bootlike ankle shoes were still on his feet. Kick them off? He wanted to, but thought better of it. The deadly yellow viper infested this plain. Suddenly, his free hand lifted to his head. A wan smile showed his relief. Made of poor-quality velvet, the same reddish-brown shade as his doublet and breeches, his beret at least was where it belonged. That he should care about that was not really odd, for he adhered strictly to Spanish customs of courtesy. Alone or in a crowd, outdoors or in, at Mass, even at his own table, the sixteenth-century Spaniard was required by custom to keep his head covered. To this rule there was one exception: he must bare his head in the presence of the king.

With disgust and self-reproach, John eased his sack to the dust and halted long enough to tie the cord at the collar of his shirt, to button doublet and canions. Panting

and perspiring, he once again blotted his glistening face
with a damp and wrinkled square of stout cotton, replaced
the sackload of books and religious wares on his shoulder,
grimacing with pain as he did so.

Then on again. Helplessly drowsing on his feet, he
stumbled, bumped into rocks, was clawed awake by cactus
thorns or bristly, sword-shaped aloe leaves. He walked a
few steps, then stopped, assailed by spells of dizziness, and
while he waited for the fit to pass, the sun's rays flayed
him pitilessly. Another ten paces, another pause. And all
the time the sharp edge of a crucifix in the sack pierced
through the cloth of his doublet into his shoulder. He
locked his lips to keep a cry from slipping through, but
shift the sack he would not. However confused he was
about all else, he was mindful that Christ carried His
gibbet over His right shoulder. The reminder was powerful enough to wrench him from the temptation to trans-
fer the load to his other shoulder.

Still, the ache in his shoulder was as nothing to his
sudden thirst. Futilely he hoped that, by some miracle,
water, just a thread of water, would appear. It appeared,
but only in his mind. He tried to pray away the shining
sorcery of flowing crystal. The Hail Mary, the prayer that
was always on his lips, sounded as strange to him as if he
had not said it in many years. He said, "Try harder. Hold
on to the words. Don't let them slip away from you." John
spoke to himself as to another person. Regardless of the
rebuke he gave himself, it was no use. He prayed only
with his lips. His thoughts strayed, now to shade and
water, now to the night-dark chapel where a single star
of light dimly illuminated the figure of the scourged
Christ.

Dragging his way through this forlorn desert of silence,

the image became more real to John than the ground he
walked upon. It seemed to stagger forward with him. Always stirred to the depths by the Divine Passion that ended
with three nails and a cross, it was the devotion that John
loved most. Every day for years he had read the Passion
according to Saint John; every day he pleaded to be permitted to partake a little of that Passion. That he was
experiencing an echo of it in himself here in this scorched
and lonely plain did not occur to him. Still less would he
have believed that, from this day forward, he was to share
in it daily, until death. John, who called out incessantly
to Christ: "Lord, Lord, hear me! Direct my feet in Your
way!" was being directed and did not know it.

He knew only that, all of a sudden, a thin, salt-tanged
wind was fanning his face. He roused like one newly
awakened. There, far below, lay the low-rolling Mediter-
ranean, dark green, light green, many shades of green, all
flecked with foam. Or was it a wind-whipped meadow of
mingled greens, overgrown with white flowers that broke
up and changed their shapes with every gust of wind? It
was the sea, though curiously unreal after the brassy plain,
which spread out far behind him. Having lost count of
time, John had no clear memory of when he left the
tediously level land and began to climb his way into the
wavy uplands. On the return trip, he promised himself,
he would be more attentive. A useless promise. John had
crossed the plain for the last time.

Presently, he was on a familiar height. It was different
from the others because here the main path became a
three-pronged fork. One prong pointed to a ledge that
overhung the sea; the middle one led on, up and up and
up, to Tarifa; the third curved off into a little woodland
alcove. From the ledge, he looked out over the water to-

ward the rambling, rocky coast of North Africa, with the cloud-shaped Atlas mountains stacked up behind it. But the view was blurred by haze. For a few minutes he thought of Father Mateo and then, less happily, of the poor apostate he had wanted to rescue. Abruptly he left the ledge, as though to turn his back on an old longing.

On the main track, he gazed upward. That blotch of dazzling whiteness on the crest of a distant bluff was Tarifa. Even as the plain had seemed to extend itself, so too the ancient town that faced Tangier appeared to float farther and farther away. Reluctantly, he pictured the steep and narrow trail that zigzagged up and around, a long, long way up and around. Was Tarifa his goal? He wasn't sure. He was sure of but one thing: he wanted to rest a while. Despite the sense of shame the desire gave him, he walked into the clearing where a wild acacia threw a thin green shade over a flat-topped boulder. Stifling a moan, he removed the sack from his shoulder, propped it against one end of the rock, then settled himself on the top. Too tall to stretch out on it, he wrapped his arms about his drawn-up knees and rested his head on them. He slid into sleep as into a pool of deep green water.

The wind blew a little harder. Leaves clashed together lightly, in whispers. Cicadas sent up their screeching song of heat. Golden bees barred with ebony set a-hum wild thistles, blue borage, vanilla-smelling broom, the bronzey green stems beaded with small, canary-yellow flowers. It was these sounds that woke him up. Was he dreaming? He must be, he thought, as he saw butterflies in fantastic numbers dipping, rising, flying apart, then streaming all together again. Above him, in the acacia, a bird piped incessantly, like a flutist leading a procession to some ceremony.

How extraordinary! John looked at all this commotion as at a pantomime. But what was its meaning? A few minutes ago the clearing was a quiet, pleasant spot. Now it had something close to bewitchment. "Nonsense," he said aloud. "All nonsense! I've never had an eye for nature. What I'm seeing now must be quite commonplace. Birds sing. Butterflies and bees swarm to flowers. Still, where did they come from all of a sudden? They were lurking in the thornbrush. To whom are the shrubs and weeds and grasses bowing? Bowing! What a fantasy! The wind is leaning against them. It's bound to arch them over." With a yawn and a stretch, he said, "I'm wasting time. I ought to be on my way." He did not move. The bird behind the lacy foliage had changed from plaintive piping to a clear, high whistling, as though it were sending out a signal or urging someone to this grove. The humming and shrilling became louder, too. Though altogether different, the insect racket reminded him of the way sheep murmur and bleat with increasing confusion when the shepherd draws near.

"Are those winged things flying to the opening of this clearing, or do I imagine it?" Whether he imagined it or not, his gaze followed and fastened itself to them.

John gave a start. Like the butterflies, his heart responded with a wild fluttering. "It isn't possible," he said. "Not here. Not alone." He shut his eyes, opened them. The white glimmer was still there. A white shirt, all torn. White breeches. In the pale gold hair the bees were drops of shining amber. Butterflies made little splashes of color on the ragged shirt.

Unaware of himself, he got off the rock. Erect and tense, he stood under the flung green lace of the acacia tree. Without knowing why, he swept off his hat. He surprised himself by flinging it to the top of his sack. Immeasurably taller than that fragile little wisp of a being, he remained rigid, hardly daring to breathe for fear of frightening him. He isn't real, he thought. Oh, but he is. He is real and he is poor. And lovely beyond words. To come upon a child of such beauty in this wilderness!

John would have believed that anything was possible now, almost anything except whose son it was who caught his enraptured gaze, came up to him, unafraid, and, reaching for his hand, reached right up into his heart.

# SEVEN

JOHN knelt on the ground before the boy and sat on his heels the better to talk to him. But for a long moment, words failed him. He could only gaze and marvel. Gently, he swung the small hand that still lay in his own. Strange, John was thinking, that this child who looked like a princeling out of a nursery tale should be wandering alone, come to him as to a friend, and come as if he wanted badly to be taken to his heart. As though he could guess John's thoughts, the boy came closer and inclined his head invitingly toward the broad right shoulder. Shyly, almost, John pressed the beautifully modeled head to his shoulder, feeling its warmth, which he was to remember for as long as he lived.

Quietly he asked, "What is your name, little brother?"

The child raised his head and gave John a piercingly sweet look, but spoke no word. Instead, he leaned against the young man and fingered the row of jet buttons that marched down the front of his doublet. His lips, red as pomegranate seeds, opened on the slightest and most pensive smile.

"Did you come here all by yourself?"

"Yes, señor."

"Do you live nearby?" John asked him, even though he could not recall ever having seen a dwelling within miles of this wood.

70

The large gray-blue eyes avoided his. The finger still traced tiny circles around the rims of the buttons.

"You didn't just fall out of the blue, did you?" John's tone was lighter than his heart. He was troubled. Somehow he must find out where this little boy belonged and take him home. Who was he? A son of impoverished nobility? Perfectly formed, the patrician delicacy of the sensitive face, the fair complexion, the pale bright hair denied any resemblance to the wiry, brown-skinned peasant children in the sun-baked regions of Spain. How old was he? Five years? Six? Seven? Choosing his words carefully, John put these questions to him. To each the boy answered nothing. He was, it seemed to John, as rich in secrets as a hive was in the gold of honey. Taking the small chin in his hand, he looked down into the unchildishly sober eyes. "Little brother, did you stray too far from home? Are you lost?"

No, he was not lost.

John's anxiety grew with a new thought that came to him. "You must tell me the truth, little brother," he said, as he held the child off from him and searched his face with his own vividly penetrating black eyes. "Have you run away from home?"

He shook his head.

John sighed. "Your mother knows where you are?" he asked, as he twisted a ringlet of soft and golden hair around his finger.

Yes, his mother knew.

Although the corners of his mouth etched themselves into a slow smile, worry deepened in John. Once more he drew the child to his side, held him in the crook of his arm. "I must be on my way," he said, "but I cannot leave you in this wood alone. You are such a little boy." Glancing toward the path, he added, "Scarcely anyone travels that trail. No, I could not let you stay here. Do you know which way to go to get home?"

"Yes, señor."

That voice! Two words plucked on a harp string. John could not take his eyes off him or keep from touching him. Stroking the curly hair, he said, "Show me which way it is."

The child gestured vaguely.

Eyes following the small, narrow hand, John laughed a little. "That way," he said, imitating the gesture, "could mean all the way to Cadiz or straight up to the sky." Indefinite though the motion was, it seemed to indicate a southerly direction.

Just then, a drift of yellow-dotted, white butterflies flew before his vision. They took his attention from the trail and led it to the child's feet. Poising airily on his insteps and ankles, their wings swung open and shut, open and shut, like spangled white satin doll fans. Head down, John was suddenly upset. "Let me see your feet," he murmured, and scattered the butterflies with a wave of his hand. "Little brother, were you running in the thornbrush?" Seriously, he examined the cuts and stone bruises, scratches made by thorns, the drops and trickles of dried blood. He gazed absorbedly, as when he meditated the nail marks on the hands and feet of the Christ on his crucifix. His eyes dimmed and, as though he could not help himself, he bent his head and put his lips to the wounds on the small feet. Then his fingers caressed them lightly. "Does it hurt to the touch, little brother?" With a slow shake of his head and a pleased smile, the little boy assured John that he liked the feel of his hands.

"You mustn't run about barefooted. There are snakes

and stinging insects, as well as stones and thorns." John gazed at him intently, and questioned in a musing tone, "What are we to do about your feet?" There seemed to be nothing that could be done—no salve, no bandages, no water with which to lave them. With an anxious glance at the child, who still was smiling trustingly at him, John took the small figure in his arms, rested his chin against the fair head for a second, then got to his feet with a single, easy movement.

He sat the boy on the boulder, placing him far back, so that his legs rested on it. Not knowing what prompted him, he removed his big cork-soled shoes of brownish red leather. After he had blown the dust off them, he leaned over the little boy and put them on his feet. John colored suddenly, and spoke as it were to his gaping shoes. "No! You won't do. What was I thinking of? I wasn't!" He grew redder yet when the child politely thanked him, but said the shoes did not fit.

"I can see that." He watched the small red mouth for a minute, then gave a sudden chuckle. The little boy laughed, too.

Relieving him of the heavy shoes, John half-turned from him and stared at his footgear as if at some token of a moment that moved rather than embarrassed, then amused him. Only minutes ago, he had warned the child against going barefoot. Now, for him to wear shoes when a fragile little boy went without—most likely because his parents were too poor to give him shoes—seemed to John a bitter reproach to all poor. Shamed, he vowed never again to wear shoes. He looked at the boy and smiled, saying to himself, "In imitation of you, little one, I will go barefooted and hatless for the rest of my days." The next moment, he thrust shoes and hat into the sack.

"Never mind," he encouraged, as again he confronted the quiet child and took the translucently white face between his hands, conscious of the feel of it. Cool and smooth it was, like a jasmine bud. "If my shoes are useless," he said with his kind smile, "my back is not. You cannot walk on those feet," he said, looking down at them. "I will carry you."

He waited. Doubt rippled over him, the way a still pool is faintly disturbed by a thrown pebble. Most children, he knew, retired to little hidden places where only they could go. Most small children loved secrets and secrecy. But this one withdrew into a faraway realm of his own and was more subtly than childishly secretive. There were things about him that made John ponder and bite his lip. Familiar with waifs and street urchins, this one looked as poor as an alley child. But he hadn't the forwardness of alley children. Like other waifs, he appeared to want comfort and affection; he had come to him as naturally as butterflies flew to thistle and broom, being neither timid nor inquisitive. He himself was filled with questions; the child hadn't asked a single one, not even his name, the first inquiry usually made by a child when faced with a stranger. Contrary to his spontaneous tenderness, his reserve would have done credit to the wisest man. Regarding questions, he was amazingly taciturn. Bashfulness it could not be, for such replies as he chose to make he made promptly, if in but two words: *No, señor. Yes, señor.* For the rest, a nod or a shake of that proud, lovely head, or a smile. And these, it struck John, implied more than words could say. For instance, when he had asked: Who are you, little brother? the sparkling smile that answered him, at least so it had impressed him, seemed to say: I cannot tell you that. But I know *you.* How silly of me! John thought, and gave a queer, helpless little laugh. Since noon, he reminded himself, he had entertained odd ideas and experienced odd feelings. With his normal energy restored, he was not sure, even, whether he had endured great fatigue or merely imagined it. Perhaps he had fasted too long. When he reached Tarifa, he promised himself, he would eat something.

Tarifa. The thought of the place drew him back to the moment. Will he go with me? John wondered, as he gazed down at the child who was silent as the rock he sat upon—sat with a kind of kingliness, despite his torn shirt and discolored feet. Sweet and small though he was, it was plain enough that he had a mind and a will of his own.

"Little brother," John said softly, "I have work to do. I cannot remain longer. Will you be a good child and let me take you to your mother? Yes?" he almost pleaded. . . .

In vain he waited for an answer. "Where do you live, little one? Down the slope or up? Your mother must be worrying about you. Once," he said, his tone low and tinged with regret, "I worried mine, and I made her very sad."

A wonderfully sweet smile played over the small face, as though he were sharing a secret with John. Whatever it was, it escaped the anxious giant. But when the boy neither offered nor surrendered enlightenment as to where he lived, John said the only thing left to say. "Look, little brother, let me carry you as far as you say. I will set you down wherever you please. Will you do that for me?"

"Yes, señor."

The sack balanced on his shoulder, the child astride his back, arms twined about the giant's neck, John and his small passenger left the wood. From all the countryside there rose suddenly a trilling of bird song, as at the rising of the sun. And in John's vigor there was an early morning freshness. How good to be himself again! The sack could not have troubled him less had it been empty. The child? Fluff! So airily light that, from time to time, John smiled back at him, asking, "You, little brother, are you still there?"

The Count of Oropesa's fleetest Arab steed could not have kept pace with John. Up and down he sped, down and up. He flew around bends to broad vistas of sky, sea and shore, lost them quickly as he dove into bowl-like hollows of esparto grass and prickly pear, then climbed again to stride the edge of a ridge with a sureness of step that he himself found unusual.

They met no one. Straight or curving, the course was unpeopled. He sped on in silence, except at intervals, when John broke it. Did his little traveler know that he was riding on a soldier's back? Indeed, yes, he was a soldier. Twice he'd fought for the Emperor Charles V of Spain. He even had some shining medals to prove it. That is, he used to have them. Where were they now? In a little village in Portugal, he supposed. Having been a long, long time away, he had returned to the place of his birth. The medals glittered on his chest; pieces of gold sparkled in his purse. Things were not as he had expected, so he had left his medals and his money with an aged uncle who probably was dead by now. He'd been to other places, too—Ceuta, Gibraltar. He knew a thing or two about loading and unloading cargo ships, and how to break up a mountain's rock and haul it away. What else? Well, in San Bernardo, near Seville, it was his job to test the courage of bulls destined for the ring. They belonged to a great lady, Doña Eleanor de Zuñiga. But he seldom saw Doña

Eleanor. A *vaquero's* place was with the bulls. Prize bulls had to be as closely guarded as the Emperor himself. The herdsman in charge of them must not let them wander out of his sight. The day long he followed them over the vast pasture lands, and at night he slept outside their corral. No, oh no, sleeping out of doors, on the ground, was not why he had left Doña Eleanor's cattle farm. He had felt, simply, that he would rather watch over people than bulls. And had he done so? Yes, God be thanked, he had. It was all very wonderful the way it happened. Walking from Seville to Gibraltar, he asked lodging for a night in a pilgrims' hospital at Ayamonte. There he lodged for not one but twenty-one nights and days, the happiest three weeks in his memory, for the hospital superior allowed him to help with the sick. If he could make a wish, what would it be? Oh, that was easy. He would wish to be always with the sick, the blind, the lame, the homeless; with unwanted children and the poor; with any and all who were downcast, helpless and weak.

More or less to himself, John talked of this and that, unaware that his stride had grown shorter and his pace was reduced to a crawl. It was not until he yawned and murmured behind his hand, "Yes, I should like to give my strength to the weak," that it occurred to him how weak he himself was. Not again! he thought with alarm, and his mind seized upon one word: *Why?* The pounding of his heart knocked the breath out of him. A flood of fire seemed to rain down from Heaven; perspiration burst from his every pore. Over and over, a small hand brushed away the glistening drops. Cool as snow-cooled water was that slight, white hand. And yet, the touch of the fingers pierced through John's whole being. They might have been arrows tipped with flame that warmed but did not burn.

Then, suddenly, his thoughts were fixed, not on the hand but on the slight body which had become an appalling weight upon his back. John struck himself a sharp blow on the forehead, as though to slap away fancies that plagued him. To no avail, the slap, for the weight of that leaf-fragile body grew heavier and heavier. He insisted, "It simply cannot be. A tiny boy bend me over double? As impossible as to add up the waves of the sea." Nevertheless, this thing he was trying not to believe was not to be denied. Bewildered, to himself he said, "He is heavier than I can endure. I cannot carry him much longer. Mother of Heaven! I, a giant with the strength of rock, I cannot uphold a child who has no more weight than a moth? No, no, no, the idea goes against all reason!"

Had his mind not been as numb as his limbs, John might have remembered another giant who, in ancient times, suffered considerable difficulty fording an angry river, all because of the leaden weight of a little Child perched on his shoulder. Still, even if he'd been alert, John's humbleness would not have permitted him to liken his present experience to that of Saint Christopher.

John had not anticipated anything as incredible and unnerving as this. Was he dreaming? He could believe he was were it not for the fact that stones and gravelly earth had torn and cut his feet and, from time to time, a narrow snow-and-fire hand flicked perspiration from his brow and face. Sometimes the hand patted his shoulder, as if to give him heart, yet caused him only humiliation that every step should cost him a huge effort. Dazedly he followed the bruising trail. Still no sign of Tarifa, which had looked so near. Still no word from the child that he wished to be put down. What had seemed as awful as it could be was now becoming worse.

Suddenly, a tumult of tinkling spread through the silence. John halted. Water straying over stones? He searched his memory for a brook. No, he was certain there wasn't one, not here. Only the wind, he thought, blowing leaves about. Achingly, he hobbled the path that led off from the one he was on and soon came to a hollow where broken stones and pin-sharp twigs, dry and woody, gave way to silky grass with water drops in the blades. All of a sudden, it was there before him. Brook water! Splintering over rocks, it scattered its cold crystal on grass and on pungent plants that edged its banks.

Can I believe it? John wondered. So much had happened for which he could find no explanation that now he was not sure that water was water. But water it was, for he felt the wetness of the grass under his cut, bare feet and breathed in the smell of moist earth, of wild mint and creeping thyme, the leafage dripping jewels of water, icy clear. Thanks be to God! The bliss of it! Had Heaven come down here?

"Let's rest a bit, little brother," he said. Still short of breath from the effort of carrying the impossibly heavy child and feeling stiff as the wooden image in the wayside chapel far behind, he managed nevertheless to crouch on the ground. As careful of the boy as though, at a touch, he might disappear, he set him down. He smiled to conceal the perplexity that now tormented him almost as greatly as had the child's weight. In no wise changed, the tiny figure stood near him, as close as possible. John longed to ask a question. He looked it at him instead. But the quiet gray-blue eyes, large and shining in the luminously pale face with its small red mouth, told him not a thing, except what he already knew, and that was that he loved all children but this one he loved extravagantly. The boy laced his fingers in John's. So still were they both that a dragonfly, dipped in liquid opal, poised on the man's knee. In front of them, the stream rushed along; behind them, birds twittered in a tree with leaves like pointed green flames, the branches crowded with cream-white cups of flowers into which the sun was pouring rose-colored light.

"Shall we go together to the brook and drink?" asked John. "No? You aren't thirsty? I can't understand that." John laughed softly. "Little brother, I am as thirsty as that dry road we walked—for how long?" Like the dragonfly, the child hovered at John's knee, looking up at him with eyes that said he thirsted only for love. As if he felt the thought, John held the boy close to him, feeling the small bones through the rent shirt. "I'll tell you what," he said, with a glance at the flowering tree, "while I go for a drink, you sit over there. Come, little brother." He gathered the child up in his arms, acutely conscious of his lightness once again, and took him to the tree. "Stay here," he said, "until I come back. I won't be long."

John cupped his hands and drank and drank. He removed his doublet, rolled up his sleeves, and, with wild relief, sank his long arms into the swirling coldness, splashed water over his head and face, then stood in the brook, letting the glacial water bathe his feet. In a very ecstasy of deliverance from pain, he called out, "Be you for ever blessed, little brother, for leading me to this stream." He paused for a moment to look at a patch of sky reflected in the glassy water. Then, with a pang of remorse, he remembered the child's bloodied feet. "Little brother, come here and I will wash the blood off your feet. This is clean, clear water."

There was no reply, only a humming gust of wind that

ruffled the glinting water. Behind him, the silence was
somehow different, too stressed. Even the birds had ceased
to twitter. The hollow seemed empty, except for himself.
Alarm stood in his eyes, as he thought: Has the little one
fled? "Oh, no!" he cried out desperately. "Do not, do not
run away!" Heart jumping in his breast, he leapt onto the
bank and there he remained, staring in amazement. *That*
child, that vision of a child caught as in a web of light
that appeared to come, not from the sun but from himself,
that was *his* little friend? John could hardly take it in. He
held his breath for fear the radiance, the small boy who
was all burnish and brilliance, would fade from his sight
like a dream.

Was it a dream? Was it fatigue and fasting that caused
him to feel curiously small, reduced to nothing, in the presence of a very little boy who but a while ago bore down
upon him with the weight of what, at times, had seemed to
be the world? John gave himself a stiff shake. Thoughts—
crazy thoughts! He wasn't certain, even, if the weight and
the child existed outside his imagination. "If only I knew!
I have never sensed or seen anything like this before. I am
so confused," he said, and ran his hand distractedly through
his thick black hair. "Do, please, say something," he
pleaded in a hushed tone. "Just a word, so that I can
trust my eyes, and my mind."

A moment later, John could feel himself going pale. His
dark eyes widened, intent upon the child who quite suddenly lifted his right hand. In the upraised palm of his
hand lay an open pomegranate. The seed-chambers glistened as with row upon row of rubies, and from the lobed
crown of the fruit there shone a cross of gold.

A pomegranate surmounted by a golden cross? Hallu-
cination, John thought. Mad—I am mad! He listened to

the thought with horror. Presently, he was listening to a silvery little voice that he recognized. But now, instead of "No, señor, yes, señor," it said in Spanish:

"*Juan de Dios, Granada será tu cruz.*"

John of God, Granada will be your cross.

Hands gripped together as if he were struggling for self-control, John stammered to the sweetly smiling Child, "You knew me all the time? Who told you my name is John?" The gaze that met his said: "I Myself have named you. Not John but *John of God.*" The divinely given name crashed against John's heart and threw him to his knees.

For a moment, he could think only of puzzling out the message. Granada. Spanish for pomegranate. Pomegranate: the floral emblem of Spain. In Holy Writ, the symbol of charity; in Christian lore, the symbol of Christ's Passion. The cross atop the pomegranate signified sacrifice and salvation.

The hollow became strangely still. When at length John dared to open his eyes, the Christ Child was gone. He saw a little cloud of golden haze shimmering above the tree where the Light of the world had stood. That was all. Flowing water was the only sound, that and John of God's low voice murmuring over and over, "Granada will be your cross."

# EIGHT

THE twentieth of January, 1537, was unlike any other in Granada's history. Even as the sky's sunset hues faded away, and the snows on the Sierra Nevada crags turned from seething pink fire into illusory silver vapor, so too the gaiety that always marked this day disappeared as with the sun. For ages and ages, *Granadinos* and their neighbors, who came in droves to the epic old city from the province, celebrated the Feast of Saint Sebastian, the early Milanese soldier who survived a flock of arrows that leapt at him from the bows of the master archers of the Emperor Diocletian. On this day, and night, merrymaking scattered the brooding dreaminess that otherwise was as typical of Granada as the Alhambra Palace on its cliff above the flowing Darro.

The *Zacatín*, the main street of trade, was deserted, shops were closed, shutters bolted, doors barred as against some stalking terror. Nearby, the *Vivarambla*, central plaza, seemed scarcely livelier than the Zacatín. Granada lay as muffled in silence as the occasional Moor, who, swathed in his ghostly white mantle, passed without sound into some shadowed alley. Though profoundly quiet, a subdued sense of excitement, tinged with shock, permeated the atmosphere. A few Granadinos grimly strolled the plaza in pairs, more like guards than men on holiday. Farmers from the lush plain of Granada, the *Vega*, and mountain men from the towns in the Sierra Nevadas loitered in groups. Such talk as they made was murmured and indistinct. In the background, close to the cathedral doors, their uneasy wives and children waited, eager to go home.

Nerves still jerked. Minds still pictured a gaunt giant with a solemnly handsome face, pale yet aglow, as if a hidden flame smoldered within him. None could forget the pensive eyes, the gentle smiles which he reserved, it had seemed, for the ragged urchins who savagely poked, mimicked and stung him with fistfuls of pebbles. Toward child, youth or man he made no hostile move, offered no resistance to the cruelty he suffered at their hands for the better part of the day. Instead, the supposedly demented peddler of books and religious goods blessed his tormentors and encouraged whatever anguish they could think to give him. He in turn stripped his little open-air stall near the Elvira Gate, at the entrance to Granada, of books, holy pictures, statues, rosaries and medals and gave them to his persecutors. His meager savings he divided among the poorest onlookers in the dumfounded mob that watched him, and, last of all, he gave to a crippled beggar his spotless shirt and doublet.

A pity, more than one spectator thought, that so kindly a man must take leave of his senses. For mad he was, utterly mad. Who but a lunatic would tear up and down streets, circle plazas, zigzag from one to the other, hour upon hour? Moreover, however troubled in spirit, no sane man would sob the way children sob, chokingly and without restraint. No sane man would draw blood from his breast with a rock and scream a thousand times over: "Mercy, Lord, mercy! Have mercy on me!" And no sane man would beg others to beat him half to death, would he?

His pleading fell on willing ears. Hard fingers dug into his flesh, pulled and pushed and shook him, and while he was thrashed by a rain of sticks, the crowd egged on the men and boys who abused him, and then baited the victim with words as piercing as nails. Battering and insults provoked not a murmur out of him. He abandoned himself to hurt and mockery like a saint to ecstasy. But for his sins he wept loudly.

The throng that trailed him the day long marveled at his stamina and patience. It pondered too, why, when "Madman! Madman!" was dinned into his ears a faint smile touched his lips, as much as to say: So that is what they think. He had looked from one to another and then appeared to have decided something for himself. The very notion of a maniac resolving a matter to his obvious satisfaction froze the hearts of the bravest. The same shocked expression stood on every face. It said: Now he is meek. But there is a strange power underneath that meekness. Who knows what he intends to do? Like that! in a split second he may become a menace. He ought to be put away.

Earlier than they would have done in other circumstances, outsiders turned homeward. They hurried from the city by way of the Elvira Gate, or by crossing the old bridges that arched Granada's two rivers, the Genil and the Darro. Granadinos crept home cautiously. The few who lingered half-hid themselves in the shadows. And even now, in the quiet blue dusk, the air seemed charged with the oft-repeated cry for mercy, with convulsive sobbing. Or was it river water rushing under the bridges?

It must be that, for, well over an hour ago, the Crazy One fell forward on the stones of the Vivarambla and lay as one dead. His pursuers stood round him in a silent circle, broken suddenly by two hidalgos who ordered them away.

They lifted the stranger. He sagged, barely able to stand. When last seen, his long arms hung limply about the shoulders of his rescuers, who took him to the Hermitage of Saint Sebastian, where Father John of Avila was staying.

Unknowingly, the renowned preacher had brought all this to pass. At the Archbishop's request, Father John of Avila had delivered the sermon that morning at the church of Saint Sebastian. Heaven, he had said, was not to be had for the taking. One must earn it by service to God. The Christian who hoped to reserve for himself even the least place on the outermost rim of Heaven must repent and atone, repent and atone, again and again and again. Long before the priest had finished, the Crazy One's distress was heard, for he wept like one who has glimpsed his own doom. Prostrating himself, his stabbing cries slashed the hush of the startled congregation, as he implored God's forgiveness and the intercession of the Blessed Virgin. The last man to make a scene, the last to consciously draw attention to himself, he became a public spectacle. Suddenly overcome by an urge more compelling than logic, he got rapidly to his feet and ran out of the church.

It was then that he began his distracted running about. The compulsion that demanded this ordeal of him forced him to uncover his soul in public, to be stripped of every shred of pride by the mob's jeering, even as Saint Sebastian let the archers divest him of his armor, bind him half-naked to a tree and use his body as a target for their arrows.

Such a swarm of faces confronted the giant that, at times, it seemed they had fused like lumps of warm wax and become somehow molded into one huge, staring countenance. He could not isolate strangers from the handful of Granadinos who frequented his book stall.

They, in turn, could not believe their eyes. This air-clawing, mercy-screaming man was the soft-spoken book-seller of the night-black eyes that held within their depths a gaze of Christlike sadness? The dreamer who quietly entreated passers-by to read and meditate the Passion of Our Lord According to Saint John, to imitate Him in His sufferings? Offered with or without purchases, his brief sermons that always urged love of the Cross were as hard to forget as the man himself. At best, he was not a fluent or even a very willing speaker. Yet let him picture the Passion and death of Christ, and words poured from him in a flow of simple eloquence.

The wandering eccentric with the grimy, tear-stained face, body and breeches splotched with blood, soiled with mud and spittle, bore hardly any likeness to the always immaculate peddler. His customers, who followed him in his wild meanderings today, agreed that on two subjects in particular their favorite vendor was a fanatic: dirt and idleness. Imprudently, though politely, he declared to beggar, duke or monk, to anyone at all, that filth breeds disease and idleness sin. A futile message. Dirt was everywhere. One took it for granted. As for idleness, you could argue for ever and not make him see that idleness was freedom and that work was meant for slaves. Admittedly, he had radical notions on these subjects, yet they were timid whispers compared to his present ravings.

If indeed they were his! It was too fantastic, the cool-headed, untalkative vendor making a scandal of himself and bringing down upon his head the revilements of a whole city. Could they be mistaken? After all, strangers of every description had streamed into Granada for the day. There might be another who resembled him. Another man cast in the same mold? As tall, as thin, as black-haired and black-eyed? With the same hands, long and sensitive, the kind of hands that Spanish painters gave to saints? Some thought this possibility as unlikely as to find a dark-skinned Moor who had washed himself white. Besides, assume that such a thing could have happened, how explain a stranger racing to the bookseller's stall and distributing his wares and savings? Or maybe that was not as odd as it seemed. The maniac's stress on penance and sin, his cries for God's mercy pointed to excessive piety, undoubtedly a trick of the fiends that commanded him. Victims of demonic possession usually went to one of two extremes: they profaned all that was holy, or they affected great devotion. Thus, for the madman to have singled out a religious goods stall seemed in keeping with the nature of his madness. As for the peddler himself, wherever he was in the scramble of people, he was far too sensible to make a bad situation worse. Rather than challenge a man possessed, he would sooner lose everything and begin anew.

Another detail added credence to this theory of mistaken identity. The peddler was an avid reader. When he wasn't engrossed in the Bible and the *Imitation,* he absorbed himself in old herbals, books on surgery and anatomy, and his thumbed copy of Pope John XXI's *Little Treasury of the Poor*. It wasn't reasonable, was it, to think that a man with his passionate interest in the art of healing would deliberately make of himself one big, bleeding welt? It was not. So, regardless of what they saw and heard, they tried to convince themselves that the madman was not the peddler, John Ciudad.

And to an extent they were right. It was not John Ciudad. It was John of God, a name and saint that nobody knew.

# NINE

THE Feast-day crowd saw in John of God a
man possessed of a devil. Father John of Avila saw a man
possessed of boundless love for Christ Crucified. Mad? Yes.
He was afflicted with that sublime madness of the saints
which defies and disturbs all the rules of logic and shows
itself in wild, sometimes horrifying behavior. To the ordinary Christian eye, this is lunacy. To a priest gifted, as was
John of Avila, with an extraordinary inwardness of eye,
it is the madness that blazes up from a burning, all-con-
suming love of God. The victim of this love cannot but
lose sight of himself at times and seem to be an entirely
different person, for he sees God alone, and *is* a different
person, breathing, moving, reliving in himself the agonies
of Christ in such a degree that he is outside of himself and
within his Master. John's crazy runs through Granada
impressed the unenlightened as precisely that: crazy runs.
The famed confessor saw them for what they were: John's
relentless pursuit of nothingness.

Although a young priest, John of Avila already had considerable familiarity with the minds and conduct of mystics
and future saints. Among those whom he directed and
was yet to direct were Saint Teresa of Avila, Saint John of
the Cross, Saint Peter of Alcantara, Saint Francis Borgia,
and Father Louis of Granada, the Dominican theologian
and writer who was to become his biographer and, later,

the Venerable Louis. Sought after throughout Spain as a
preacher, his fame as a spiritual director surpassed that
of his sermons. His shining wisdom guided souls to sanctity
with the piercing directness of the star that led the shepherds and the Magi to the crib of the infant King at Beth-
lehem. This reader of souls detected their capacities and
needs as easily as others distinguish the features of faces.
With similar ease, he offered advice, and always it was
immediately forthcoming and positive.

Always until now. John of God's spiritual dimensions
had exceeded his imposing physical stature. His zeal for
encouraging a whole town to humiliate him, to give him
some of the agony of the Sacred Passion, his tremendous
ardor for penance were so fiery as to confound the great
confessor. Having confessed John, he counseled him in
every respect but one. John had begged for permission to
perform a certain penance. The request put the saint-
maker in a quandary. This time, his dependably lucid
judgment was befogged by unsureness. This time, his answer had not burst upon the penitent with the clarity of
light. There was no answer—yet.

Nine out of ten confessors, he suspected, would be swift
to forbid it. But John of Avila found himself as curiously
reluctant to resist as to allow it. If he were certain that it
would uplift, not crush John's sensitive spirit, that good,
not disaster, would result, that the excessive penance he
craved might not indeed cause true madness, then he would
sweep aside every argument against it. But how was one to
foresee the outcome? Time alone would tell. The question was what would it tell? For sheer frightfulness it was
unprecedented. To permit or not to permit John to subject himself to so inhuman an ordeal was neither an easy
nor a comfortable matter to decide.

It was during the priest's silent shuttling from no to yes and back to no again that John of God, suddenly sensible of the conflict in his confessor, withdrew from the wall crucifix where he had been kneeling and approached the priest quietly, as if he wished to help but did not know how.

Holding his head in his hands, hunched over the small writing table at which he sat, Father John of Avila dropped his hands and peered up at his penitent, hoping against hope that he had changed his mind of his own accord. The placid, long sweet look that John gave him told him the opposite. "I have upset you, Father," he said apologetically. "Had I known that I'd give you a moment's concern, I would not have let those gentlemen bring me to you."

"No?" The priest smiled a little. "I think God intended it to be. One way or another, you would have come to me." He laid a hand on John's arm. Hard as rock, that arm, and as cold. But that head, he knew, was ablaze with one idea. "I am concerned," he admitted. "The minute you came into this room," he said, trying for lightness, "I expected trouble. But I like you." He paused. No words could express how much he liked him. Who could help liking such a spirit, such an inner glory that his humility exposed rather than concealed, in much the way that the night sky shows up the glowing radiance of moon and stars?

The mutual trust and affection that flashed between the future Blessed John of Avila and the future Saint John of God, the instant they met, needed no words from either one. Each was quick to sense when he was liked and each responded openly to understanding and affection.

Freeing his hold on John's arm, the priest motioned toward a chair. "Sit down, John. Let's talk a bit. I should

like to know more about your childhood, your family.
Come closer," he said, when John remained a little away
from him. Obediently, John drew the rush-bottom chair
right up to the table and sat stiffly on the edge of it. Overcome by the famous priest's kindness to him, he looked
down and nervously fingered a black wooden rosary that
was wrapped around his wrist.

For a moment, John of Avila forgot everything for staring at John's black, magnetic eyes. Their strange listening,
waiting look seemed more pronounced than before. The
man who made his penance on his knees before the crucifix
was a mystic, lost in God. The man sitting tensely on the
chair's edge was a child that was afraid of what it was going
to hear.

"Well, now, let us speak of you. That is why we both are
here." The priest regarded the young man with a benign
expression. "By birth, you are a Portuguese—"

Nodding, John took a deep breath and went back into
time, back to Montemor-o-Novo. "I was an only child.
I grew up in an atmosphere of piety and love. My father
and mother were devout Catholics." He hesitated, then
stumbled on again. "My mother was especially pious. The
first words she taught me were not Father and Mother but
Jesus and Mary. As soon as I could speak, she taught me
two short prayers. They are, I think, the outstanding
memory of my childhood." His face turned away from the
priest, John murmured: *"Com Deus me deito, Com Deus
me alevante—* That is about all the Portuguese that I remember. It means: With God I sleep, with God I rise. The
other prayer was almost as simple:

> "Blessed be the light of day,
> Blessed be my Creator,
> Blessed be the Son of the Virgin Mary."

"It is easy," said the priest, "to see what kind of a woman she was."

"A simple village woman, Father, but I have never met her equal in goodness. She was good to everybody, too good."

"And your father?"

"A kindly, honest, warmhearted man. But it was my mother who was my guide. I looked up to her as to a saint. Whatever she said, or asked of me, I accepted without question."

"Did she ever express a hope that you would one day be a priest?"

"No, never. However, shortly before she died, she told my father that it was the will of God that he should join the Franciscans."

"Did he?"

"Yes, he became a Franciscan Brother at the Convent of Xabrega, in Lisbon, where he died."

"You saw him before his end?"

John said hoarsely, "I was too late for that, too late for everything. Too late," he said again.

The small room was utterly silent and almost dark, except where a lamp of beaten copper threw a pale amber mist over the bone-white Christ nailed to a black cross. The priest leaned forward, intently watching John, who tried to conceal the old, old sense of guilt that still darkened his soul. "Go on," he said gently.

"You must wonder why I was so many years returning to the place of my birth. From the day I ran away from home, I thought of nothing but the day that would bring me back. I sent messages home with travelers who passed through Oropesa. For years I sent messages. But I never had word from Montemor. I concluded they did not want me back. God knows, they would have had reasons enough for not wanting me back. Nevertheless, I saved my wages and planned to return to look after my parents."

"It was how long before you carried out that plan?"

"More than twenty years, Father. After military duty in the Holy War against the Turks, in Austria-Hungary, I made a pilgrimage to Santiago de Compostella, and then went home." With raw anguish, he said, "I lived for that day, worked for it, saved for it, fought for it. I wanted to make reparation. God denied me the only act that would in part have redeemed my wickedness." After a pause, he continued. "Our house was on the *Rua Verde do Arrabalde*. When I reached the door, I peeped through the latticed opening. Within, all was neglected. I struck the knocker against the door, and soon a slovenly woman came scuffling across the patio. She was a stranger to me. She had never heard of Andres and Teresa Ciudad. I asked if I might go in and look around. That was a mistake. The house was bleak, thick with dust and fallen plaster. The shining kitchen that had been my mother's was sooty from charcoal smoke and stained with grease. The shelves were empty. The bread chest that my mother polished as though it were silver was crusted with dirt and filled with old rags. After I left, I walked street after street, knocked at door after door, putting the same question, receiving the same answer. By sundown I was still searching, still trying to find someone who knew my parents and could tell me where they were. Then, on my last visit to the church of Santa Maria do Bispo, I saw a white-haired, elderly man lighting candles at the Altar of Pardons. He was my uncle, my mother's brother, Alfonso Duarte."

"Was it he who told you where they were?"

The voice that reached the priest seemed to come from

the deepening shadows. "Yes, Father, he told me. My mother died a few weeks after my disappearance. My father died a few years later." John lifted grieving eyes to the priest. "To this day, I don't know what made me do it. I will never understand why I should give such hurt to those who gave to me nothing but love and kindness. I killed my mother as surely as if I had thrust a sword through her heart."

"No, no, no, John! Her life was in God's hands, not yours. Even the Boy Jesus slipped away from His Mother and Saint Joseph and caused them great worry, until they found Him in the temple, preaching to the Doctors."

"Our Lord had a reason," John said, unconsoled. "He told the Blessed Virgin that He must be about His Father's business."

"And how do you know, John, that He was not about His Father's business when He took you from your parents? You don't know, nor can you judge yourself."

"I know what I am. I can judge that I am nothing. Father," he said desperately, "I beg you, allow me this chance to make atonement for my sins."

"You have, John. From the age of nine you have felt the whips of conscience."

"That isn't enough. Can't you see it isn't nearly enough?"

"Look, John, tomorrow I am going home. You have had a terrible day. At the moment, you need rest and quiet. I have a small hermitage at Montilla. Spend a while away from everyone." Absently, Father John picked up the perforated box that was used for sprinkling sand on wet ink. He shook a few grains into the palm of his hand. "For meditating," he said, "Montilla is as perfect as the desert. Like the desert, it is sandy, full of light and stillness. I am always available to my friends and spiritual children. If you prefer, you need have no companion but God." He blew the sand off his hand, put the box back in its place. John's fingers, he noticed, fidgeted more and more with the rosary beads, and his eyes were fastened upon the little crucifix.

"Well, John?"

He replied, "I cannot say yes or no, Father. It is for you to say. Do what you like with me."

Glancing for a moment out of the window at the star-studded blackness, John of Avila prayed for release from his own darkness, prayed for one little star of light to show him whether he was to lead or to follow this remarkably humble man. "You are right," he said, looking John straight in the eyes, "it is for me to say. Ah, but it is far from easy to see clearly what it is I have to do for you. This means of expiation that has you in its grip is— frightening. There is grave risk involved."

"Risk? To me?"

"John, you can't have thought beyond the moment. You won't be tolerated in the streets for long, not in the role of a madman. One day, two at best, and guards will be summoned."

"Naturally, Father. They will lock me up." There was a fearless ring in his voice, and the bruised face lit up with a smile of rare charm.

Bewildered, the priest looked at him a little without speaking. Then: "Had you not been brought to me, would you have undertaken this punishment on your own?"

"Oh, no, Father, no. I would first have consulted a priest."

"Why? You see this penance as obligatory. You implore my consent. You suffer at the thought that I may not give it. Until you came here, you were free to do as you pleased. If, as you claim, you know that this penance is required of you, why did you not spare yourself this further anguish? You have free will."

"I have, yes. But I have not the freedom to use it. I am governed by impulses and confessors."

"Was there ever anything that you very much wanted?"

John's eyes went again to his crucifix. He said nothing.

To suffer, only to suffer, thought the priest. He knows joy in suffering as others know it only in the absence of suffering. The more he suffers, the greater becomes his love and his charity. Perhaps suffering is his vocation.

"Father, I am not trying to put my will against yours. But I know that what I want for myself now will save, not destroy me."

John of Avila leaned back in his chair and put his hand over his eyes. These impulses that John spoke about, what were they but the breathings of the Holy Ghost? He remembered the words of Saint Paul: *Who would dispute the right of the Lord of choosing the means for the purifying and perfecting of His Elect?* That was enough. He knew that he must not oppose Divine authority, even if the ways of God were well past understanding. He took his hand from his eyes. John was gazing at him, smiling. The clear, inscrutable depths of those eyes! The inner radiance of him! If he continued to look at him, the priest told himself, he would forget what he had intended to say.

"John, I have accepted you," he said. "In return, you have a duty to me. You must promise always to do what I say."

"I promise, Father."

"Good! Now don't argue this," the priest said calmly, "for it is bound to happen. The time will come when you will find yourself saddened and hopelessly depressed. You are to send for me at once." The two pairs of eyes met, locked in a long glance. John's glowed, unclouded by the warning. "Even now, John, you are telling yourself that I am mistaken. You will discover the truth for yourself. Your cross lies not in the pain that you yourself must endure, but to witness the abuse of those who are truly mad, that will agonize and undo you. In this will you feel the weight of your cross. Fall under it you will, and it is then that I can help you. Not for any reason are you to hesitate. I will be waiting, ready to go to you." He rose, went to John and placed his hands on his shoulders. "Rely on God's love for you, rely on His mercy. He has begun His work. He will fulfill it."

Suffused with bliss, John knelt for the confessor's blessing.

The two stood for a moment, searching one another's eyes and finding each a friend. The tall penitent seemed to John of Avila like a soaring altar candle. He was pale and pure as wax, as radiant and weightless as flame. Before he came out of his musing, John was gone. Swiftly, courageously gone to his heaven and hell in one.

# TEN

FATHER, he is your friend, we all know that. You wanted him here. It is your house. But is it a hermitage? Not since he came. We should, or at least it used to be understood that we should, have silence. Who can have silence with him around? He makes it impossible for any but the hard of hearing to stay here," said the young pilgrim with a sullen look at Father John of Avila.

"You're cross today, Andrés." Father John smiled gravely at the youth, aware that too little sleep had made him irritable. "As for breaking the silence, suppose you try to speak more quietly. Now, who is it that makes staying here so difficult for you?"

"I don't know his name. He doesn't talk; he only prays and sobs and groans, as if he'd been thrown back to earth out of Heaven. His cell is to the right of mine."

"Oh-h." Father John nodded. The smile that flickered on his lips annoyed Andrés the more.

"If your cell were next to his, you'd be too tired to lift your mouth in a smile, to say nothing of lifting your mind in prayer. Since he came to Montilla I haven't had a night's sleep." Andrés waited hopefully, got no reply. "By my life, Father, can I help it if I'm not the marvel he is? He scarcely touches food. A few olives, a handful of grapes, a dry crust. That's all he eats, when he eats. Three days together every week he fasts from all food. And none knows better than I that he doesn't sleep. And yet, he's never tired," Andrés admitted grudgingly. "How does he do it? I am younger than he, but look at me! Look!" He called the priest's attention to the puffiness and dark shadows under his eyes. "All because I've had no sleep," he said.

There was no sound in the room except the tinkle of glowing charcoal burning in a great brass brazier that stood on a tripod set upon the blue-tiled floor. "Never before have I complained, Father," Andrés continued, "but this is too much. He doesn't go to bed, so why can't he spend the nights where he spends the days, and let other people rest?"

"Where is that? In the chapel?"

"Yes, and why not in the chapel? For hours he lies prostrate before the Holy Sacrament. For hours he keeps his forehead pressed to the nailed feet of Our Lord on the big crucifix, and for more hours yet he kneels at the altar of Our Lady of Sorrows. I mean no irreverence, Father, but that is where he belongs. He mourns his sins, he mourns with the Blessed Virgin. He is all eyes for her, like a man in love. I've seen him myself, lingering before her image, always looking, always gazing at the crystal tears on her cheeks, as though they and she were real. It gives one an odd feeling to watch him, and when he prays the Rosary, the Sorrowful Mysteries are the ones he repeatedly meditates. How do I know? I hear him. In the chapel, in his cell, he meditates aloud. Does he have to make such a disturbance?" Andrés demanded.

The priest replied, "You disturb yourself. Why are you all keyed up?"

"I've said *why*. Oh, I don't doubt that he needs to pray and sob as he does, but—" Andrés' brown cheeks went red under the other's hard gaze, and he squirmed uneasily when Father John said, *"You* don't doubt that he needs to pray! What's the meaning of that smug remark?" His glance was not paternal now. "Answer me," he said coldly.

"I mean," Andrés began uncertainly, "well, I mean that he must have some guilt on his soul. By the looks of his back, half the men in Spain have taken a whip to him. And the welts I mean are not the new ones that he gives himself every night." Unnerved by Father John's grim silence, he stammered, "It—it was wrong of me, I know, but night before last when—when that queer whizzing sound came from his cell again, I left mine and went to his door. I looked in through a crack in the wood. He was scourging himself with a discipline made of slim pomegranate wands. They're pliant as reeds and sting like fire. But it isn't that discipline that gave him the scars I saw."

Dark brows meeting over his eyes and oddly shaken, John of Avila said, "So you assume that he merited those scars for misdeeds and got them dishonorably? Just you listen to me, Andrés. He got them honorably and gloriously."

"How? Where? In battle?"

"Yes, in battle with himself."

"With himself, with an army, it's one and the same to me. All I ask is that he be isolated."

"That is enough, Andrés. Sit down. You aren't leaving yet." On guard against hotter anger in himself, John of Avila looked away from the peevish youth to the brazier that burned the November chill off the room. He stared at the fiery coals as though he saw the devil and his ways with the minds of men. He thought, he is in each of us; in my anger, in Andrés' selfishness and insolence. John alone would have welcomed the barbed words. He would justify the boy's complaint.

Calm again, he said, "You are quite right. The man—his

name is John—is a rarity, more to be marveled at than copied in his penances. But his kindness we ought to try to imitate. If he knew you were bad-tempered because his praying deprived you of sleep, he would be on his knees to beg your forgiveness." He paused, but Andrés, though he had flushed with embarrassment, still did not speak. The priest went on, "How old are you, Andrés?"

"Going on nineteen, Father." His voice was low, with an undertone of contrition.

"This is your second or third stay here?"

Andrés stifled a yawn. "My third, Father."

"Here's my advice, Andrés. Try the university. Salamanca. Alcala. Wherever you please. You will never be a good solitary. God does not ask it of you. Fortunately, He has given mankind an endless choice of callings. Holiness," he said, his voice very low, "is the heaviest of crosses."

Andrés thought a long moment. "Now, when it is too late to unsay what I said, I see how wrong and impertinent I was. I am sorry and ashamed. I, who ought to have tried harder to overcome my human weakness, was furious with him for being able to conquer his." Andrés sighed. "If," he added, "he knows what weakness is. I expect he doesn't. The man is a saint, isn't he, Father? John you called him? Yes, John is a saint."

"Quiet, Andrés, please. Careful, careful!"

Puzzled, Andrés bit down on his lip. "I guess this isn't my day, Father. No matter what I say, it is the wrong thing. May I be excused?"

"No, stay where you are," muttered the priest, and looked over Andrés' head. He was peering anxiously through the partly open door into the dim passageway. "Don't say 'saint' again," he warned, as he withdrew his glance from the door. "At about this hour of the morning,

John is apt to come in for a few minutes. Had he been out there, had he heard what you just said, goodness knows when I'd see him again. Call him a saint within his hearing, and he's gone. Like that!"

"Gone! You mean he would actually—leave?"

"Yes, actually, and with the speed of a phantom." Father John pushed a clay bowl of fruit to one side, rested his black-sleeved arms on the table top and leaned forward in his chair. "Andrés, it isn't often that I discuss one recluse with another. But there is something you need to be told. I don't think you will forget it. I never will. In the future, when you are tempted to fret about this, that and the other, this may help you to greater charity and self-control. A moment ago you asked that John be isolated."

"Yes," the young man answered faintly, "I did, and I ask your pardon."

"You have it. Andrés, John isolated himself for many months. More than an idea, it was a thing he craved, yearned for—like dry earth for rain. I gave my consent." The memory stifled the priest's words for a moment, and his fingers idled with the star-pointed crown of a pomegranate in the yellow-brown bowl.

"Where did he isolate himself?" asked Andrés curiously.

"At the Royal Hospital in Granada."

"Oh, I see. He was ill."

"He was not ill," Father John said slowly. "There was nothing the matter with him, except the affliction that is common to most saints: the need and longing to expiate sin by extreme means." Father John ceased to finger the pomegranate crown. "What John deliberately put himself through may seem shocking and abnormal from a worldly point of view, but the world forgets," said the priest, "that great acts of suffering are inspired by great love of God—

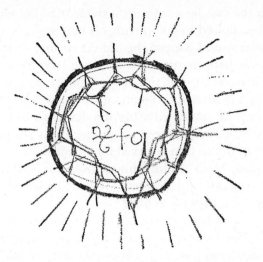

that and that alone. For most of us, it is hard enough to
imitate Our Lord's charity. The saint goes far beyond that.
Saints like John are consumed with the desire to relive in
their own bodies the agonies of the Divine Passion."

Andrés started to speak. Then he was struck by the fixed
stare on the other's face, concentrated, he did not know
why, on the reddish-purple pomegranate. He said finally,
"If John wasn't ill, why did he go to the Royal Hospital?"

"To receive the abuse that is accorded to madmen in the
name of treatment. You see, Andrés, on the Feast of Saint
Sebastian, I preached in Granada. John was in the church.
Something that I said overwhelmed him with grief. In
piercing wails, he begged God's mercy. He left the church,
ran through the streets, sobbing and shrieking, wanting the
contempt and ridicule that his behavior earned him. Understandably, onlookers thought him insane. When he discovered with what cruelty a madman is treated, he played
the part in order to be struck and stoned and spat upon.

Later in the day, he was brought to me. All that he wanted was to be allowed to go on with his pretense. He not only knew what would happen, he did everything in his power to make it happen. For two or three days he wandered about the streets, the victim of every imaginable abuse and indignity. He invited torment, and, as though to thank his tormentors, he presented a big wooden cross to be kissed. Eventually, he was dragged off to the Royal Hospital and confined in the section reserved for the mad."

The mad. Mad! Andrés shrank from the word as from a viper concealed in flowers. "What," he asked, a little fearfully, "did they do to him?"

"You saw his back, Andrés. That is what they did. They strapped him face down on the floor, or bound him to a stake and flogged him with a knotted double cord." Father John held himself very still, as if the lash were about to fall on him. "Flogging," he said, "is the accepted treatment for lunacy. That failing, iron rods, white hot, are applied. The theory still prevails that devils are the cause of insanity. If they cannot be whipped out of a body, then branding with hot irons, it is thought, will hasten their departure."

Stunned, Andrés regarded the renowned confessor with frank surprise. "I cannot question your wisdom, Father." He hesitated. "But how could you let him endure that for months?"

John of Avila did not speak at once. He only sat there, absorbed in the pomegranate. He was thinking of John's pomegranate with the golden cross, of the beautiful name that John was too humble to use or to reveal to any save his confessor. At length he answered, "It seemed to me a greater spiritual risk to forbid than to permit it. Time passed. When I had no word from him, I went to the hospital of my own accord. I envied rather than pitied him. The strength of a saint is as bewildering as his joy in suffering. Though bruised and beaten, he was dazzled, superbly sustained by the elation of imitating his Saviour bound and scourged. It was my intention to have him discharged. One word from me and he would have surrendered himself as completely to my will as to God's. Yet when I saw him, I was somehow convinced that God wanted him there a while longer."

"How long did he stay?"

"About eight months." Reading Andrés' thoughts, Father John said quietly, "Puzzling though it is, the very inability to comprehend the mystery and strength of a saint both perplexes and enlightens a confessor. One minute I wondered what to do about him, the next I knew that sense must yield to apparent senselessness. Still, it is divinely wise to save your soul. That was his battle, and he chose a madhouse for his battlefield. Love of the cross and all that it implies is in his blood and bones. More than once he has said to me, 'I am good for nothing but a cross.' He doesn't realize that zeal for suffering gives a man power over other men. Some day he will exert that power, but his humility will always veil it from himself."

"When did you see him again?" asked Andrés stiffly.

"At the end of the eighth month. I still hadn't heard from him, so I went a second time to Granada. I was in no doubt then about what to do. He had dwindled to a shadow of himself. Head to foot, he was covered with open sores, bruises and whip stripes. His wounds hadn't been cleansed or dressed. Infection had set in. He looked ill enough to be dying. In spite of the shape he was in, day after day, sometimes twice a day, his raw and bleeding flesh was torn afresh by the knotted lash."

Andrés heard this, aghast. He shuddered, as though the sharp November wind were screaming through him. "In places like that," he began, staring intently at the priest, "do the attendants keep count of the lashings they administer to the patients?"

Father John nodded, and his face expressed mingled wonder and pain. "Every fall of the whip is recorded. I asked to see John's score sheet. It seems humanly impossible, but he survived five thousand strikes."

The prism-tinkle of burning coals accentuated the hush in the room Outside, dry leaves and sand were lifted and blown about by a rising wind. Dimly there came to the two who sat in silence a roll of thunder, far away.

Father John stirred in his chair, saying, "John had more than his share. As I guessed he would, he occasionally dropped his mask of insanity. There were times when he could not endure the pitiless treatment accorded the real maniacs. It was then that he begged the attendants to show them mercy and reserve the lash for him alone. 'Heartless men,' he would say, 'why do you torture these unfortunates who are your brothers and mine? Show them compassion. Feed them properly, keep them clean, let them sleep. What use are you making of the revenues which the Crown provides for these unhappy souls?' Naturally," continued the priest, "his pleadings confirmed the suspicions of the attendants that he was not insane. Angered by his rebukes, they broke all the rules and flogged him savagely. He did not ask their pardon, only cried out, 'Strike, my brothers, strike this rebellious flesh. Harder! Harder!' Otherwise, he was silent as Christ was silent before fury and the scourges. Nor was he ever seen to flinch or twitch a muscle under the fire of the lash. Those five thousand cracks of the whips took their toll of him, but what took an even greater toll was having to witness the misery and helplessness of the truly mad. Even a saint has his limits. When I saw him the second time, I knew that John had come to the end of his endurance. He had seen too much for too long. He agonized over every huddled, frightened figure in the ward, affected overwhelmingly by their suffering. Had he died, he would have died of compassion."

For a long moment Andrés could make no sound. Profound amazement, and a new humility, kept him silent. "What happened after that?" he asked finally, his voice a little shaky.

"I told him he'd had enough, that it was time to put an end to his make-believe madness. Then I gave official confirmation of his sanity and left him there to be looked after. The same men who had flogged him brutally vied with one another to alleviate his pain. Had it been anyone but John, that would have surprised me. But he seems to have been born to inspire love in others. He himself is intensely affectionate, and generous beyond the limits of common sense. His compassion for his fellow sufferers, his extraordinary courage and faith, obviously moved the attendants to deep respect for him, for they spared themselves no effort to speed his recovery." Father John paused, wondering why he could not take his eyes off the pomegranate, nor be satisfied until he touched its hard roundness again. But he was talking and thinking of John of God. That explained it. "Within a few days," he resumed, "John was perfectly well, completely healed. The next thing I knew, he was serving the sick at the Royal Hospital. He asked for the lowliest duties and the most repulsive cases. On those poor patients that others were glad enough to let him wait upon, he lavished attention and tenderness."

"I can't picture him nursing the sick," said Andrés candidly. "It's hard for me to think of him anywhere but in a chapel or a cell."

"Only because you don't know him."

"When he's with the sick, is he mournful the way he is here?"

Father John smiled. "Quite a lot more," he answered, "but he never lets himself show it. John finds happiness in serving anyone, especially the sick. Through one of the hospital officials, I learned that, as a nurse, John is a model of competence and vivacity."

"He is?" Andrés' tone was unbelieving.

"He is," echoed the other, and smiled. "You're hard to convince. Why?"

"Oh, I'm convinced now of his—piety," Andrés assured him, careful to avoid the word he'd been warned not to breathe. "But he looks too much the visionary to be practical about anything, certainly not anything as down-to-earth as nursing the sick, let alone victims of disgusting diseases. Besides—" Andrés began, then broke off.

"Yes? Besides—what?"

"Father, he just doesn't seem very human. When he's in the chapel, I can't pray for watching him. It's not only that he kneels for hours, transfixed, before the crucifix, it isn't the desperate note of supplication in his voice when he prays to Our Lady of Sorrows; it is that luminous something about him, as though a white flame burned within him. I'd doubt my eyes, except that others have noticed it, too. Whether that peculiar radiance is always evident, I wouldn't know. Quite honestly, I observe only his back and his face in profile. If I happen to pass him going to or from the chapel, I keep my head down. I wouldn't dare confront him face to face."

Nothing answered Andrés except the hum of the wind. He sighed. "I appear to have said the wrong thing again." He looked up, to see Father John smiling.

"No," the priest said, "you've only misjudged him. John is eminently practical. With his deep spirituality he combines the most excellent common sense and a passion for work and usefulness. Far from being alien to visionaries, these characteristics are typical of the true Christian mystic. Not very human? Andrés, he is as human as love. Indeed, I've not met many men with his capacity for affection. He is aglow with love, as a summer's day is aglow with light. He loves God, he loves his neighbor, for in everyone he sees the likeness of God. This tenderness, it seems, showed itself as never before in his devotion to the sick. He loved and was loved in return."

"Why didn't he stay on, then?" asked Andrés reasonably.

The priest answered promptly, "Because he is human and is subject to pride. Doctors lauded his skill, the Supervisor praised his obedience, nurses admired his desire and ability to care for the most difficult cases. In his self-sacrificing dedication, as in all things," said Father John musingly, "he is the exception. It doesn't take long to recognize that. One day, some poor fellow who doubtless never knew such kindness as John showered on him, tightly gripped his hand and said he was a saint. Every word of praise fell on John like a shadow, but the darkest and most threatening to his humility was to be called a saint. That was that. In spite of pleadings and flattering offers, he would stay there no longer. He fled the hospital and Granada and came here to me."

Andrés gave a slight shake of his head. "In that case, how shall he ever stay anywhere?"

"I am no man to answer that question, Andrés. Time may hold the answer, time and the unexpected."

# ELEVEN

THE light in the heavens dimmed steadily and the wind roared in fitful gusts. Although he would rather not have warmed himself, simply because warmth in November was a comfort, John obeyed his confessor and drew his chair up to the brazier. He sat in motionless silence, yet with a certain look of subdued excitement on his face, which, pale and translucent as alabaster, was lifted to the long grilled oblong of the room's window. Through the carved wooden bars he could see violet clouds piling up against a sky as gray as resinous smoke shot through with flashes of greenish yellow.

Also silent, the priest's piercing eyes rested on his thinly towering friend. A deep affection had grown between the two, and to sit together without exchanging a word seemed only to accent the intimacy between them. But the calm that John of Avila usually felt in John's presence was absent now. John looked as though he had not broken his fast in a week, and under the full, gleaming black eyes were mauve hollows, marks of the sleepless, impassioned penitent whose harshness with himself knew no limits. And yet, emaciated and drained of color as John was, there smoldered within that gaunt vessel of bone and spirit a vigor that John of Avila himself could scarcely comprehend. He knew only that John's austerities fed rather than starved the vitality that burned within him.

How long could he keep it up? The apostolic preacher who urged penance upon everyone was seized suddenly by scruples and depression, not unlike John's abrupt swoops into gloom. Had he let him carry things too far? he wondered. Worse, almost, than the five thousand cracks of the whip on his back was his endless combat against the body's commonest needs, such as nourishment and rest. Sleep was his particular temptation. No night passed but he fought it resolutely. Using his power of will like a weapon, he slashed at sleep with a fierceness that in one of his gentle nature was as startling as lime-green lightning knifing through the pale blue silk of a placid summer sky. His victory was not final but neither was it small. He allowed sleep to disarm him for exactly one hour in every twenty-four. For that one hour he slept in a sitting position, leaning against a wall. This battle, the priest knew, would continue throughout John's life, unless he was ordered to capitulate. Should he say the word that would put an end to it? Once again, the eminent confessor was in doubt what to do.

As familiar with the puzzles of the nervous system as with the enigmatic soul, John of Avila pondered whether John's harsh use of his body might not in the end send him hurtling from a lofty ideal into a pit of despondency. There would be no problem, he was thinking, if the excesses a saint applies to his body in order to purify his soul affected the soul alone. But always there were brain and body, nerves and senses to regard. A cooler nature than John's might survive a saint's extreme discipline without ill effects. But the absorbed man sitting opposite him, his gaze as distant as his thoughts, was ardent, not cold. His outer aspect of reserve was but a shallow film of frost that melted quickly under the warmth of his emotions. The priest was not past believing that John's response to human misery was of a fervor that could set the world afire with his mingled grief and anger at man's indifference to his neighbor. He thought with his heart. His greatest and also his most vulnerable possession, it was easily won and easily crushed, for it reacted with rare intensity to sympathy as well as suffering. Such was his nature that he could be exalted or broken by the force of his feelings. How was one to guide him? John of Avila wasn't sure. Yet it was enough to look at him to know that he yearned for something. Not for anything outside of himself, but for something in himself that he could give to others. The answer? Not a monastery, that was certain. John showed no desire to be a priest or even a lay brother, although there was something of the priest in him. What then? John of Avila didn't know; he knew only that the time had come for John to equalize his severe spiritual exercises with practical work.

"I've been thinking," said the priest, breaking the long silence.

John seldom laughed, but when he smiled, as now, his expression was amiable and charming. "Have you? Should that surprise me?" The black pools of his eyes shone with an eagerness that told the other that he, too, had been thinking—and had something to say that he could not keep to himself much longer.

"In a manner, yes, it should surprise you," said Father John. "I've thought only so far and no farther." As he watched John's strong, slim fingers twisting the long rosary that hung about his neck, he had the feeling that anyone in pain would welcome the help of those hands.

"Some people," he went on, "have a gift for languages, some for words, some for art, for law, for medicine. God has given us a multitude of callings, without which the world would not balance. You, John, have a great gift for love and charity. How you might best use this gift, I am not certain. But once the answer comes, you and your work will be one. You will be a dedicated martyr to it." He paused, saw that what he had said imparted to John's face an expression that was almost ecstatic. Puzzled, he asked, "Have your penances and prayers given you a thought to direction?"

John spoke, and his voice was low, yet oddly excited. "I am not aware of gifts and talents, but my strength I cannot deny. Yes, I know what I want," he said, gazing at the priest intently. "I want to serve the sick poor."

Though the room was dim, he seemed alight. It was, thought the priest, as if the cloud-hidden sun had suddenly concentrated its radiance on John, pouring light over him as he himself poured charity over any and all in need of help. As he looked at the man who saw God in a hidden woodland, caressed Him, spoke to Him and carried Him as had Saint Christopher, he became mindful of the words spoken by the Christ Child: *Granada will be your cross.* "I am glad," said John of Avila simply, and drew a breath of relief. "But I shall miss you when you leave me for Granada."

John gave him a grateful smile, and now a tinge of color came into his pallid face. "Before I return to Granada," he said, "I'd like to make a pilgrimage to Guadalupe."

"Guadalupe," the priest echoed absently and glanced up at the sky that now was the color of steel. "This isn't the best season for walking to Guadalupe. The weather's apt to be cold and wet. However, I can appreciate your desire to place yourself under the protection of Our Lady of Guadalupe, and I can understand your haste. The sooner you return to Granada, the better the Directors will like it. They'll certainly rejoice to have you back."

The priest's words made a curious silence about them. John stared at the red glow of coals among gray ash and nervously fingered the smooth wooden balls of his rosary beads. "Father, you've misunderstood. I'm not going back to the Royal Hospital, not ever," he said, in a tone grown strangely firm. "Where would be the use? They wouldn't listen to the changes that I know are essential and right. Believe me, I have given this matter thought. I've thought of nothing else, prayed for nothing else." After a fleeting pause, he said, "I want to serve God in the sick poor; I want to serve them for love of Him. But I must do it in my own way, for I know that I am right. I also know that none of the officials at the Royal Hospital would respect or pay any attention to my ideas, which are the very opposite of theirs."

"Then what do you propose to do?"

"With God's help," replied John, "I will initiate the reforms I have in mind in a hospital of my own."

"A hospital of your own! Good heavens, John, what are you thinking of!" The priest was stunned at the idea.

"I'm thinking of finding a place that I can make into a small refuge. Any little house in Granada will do, at least for the time being. If it is old and falling to pieces, that's nothing. I'm not incapable of using tools. My hospital will be a place where the sick will have a chance to get well." On and on he talked, rapidly, as was his way when discussing a subject near his heart. He was vividly alive and excited, and John of Avila saw a joyousness in him that he'd never seen before. John's vision of his hospital uplifted him like a quivering dart and carried him away. But the other man was dumfounded. He sat so still that his breathing hardly moved the black cloth of his cassock. Stirred and distressed in one, it was some moments before he became aware that John's voice which, like his heart, had lifted with fervor, had faded into utter silence.

John of Avila straightened from his stooped position, and his fixed look was more anguished than astonished. "John, John," he said, as to a child who insists upon following a fancy, "I wish I needn't, but you force me to answer your impassioned dream in the language of common sense." He sighed heavily. "You had better face it," he said, "for it is a dream."

If this was a blow to John, he didn't show it, only waited patiently for his confessor to say his say.

"A hospital of your own, any little house anywhere in Granada! Don't you realize that you've nothing? You haven't a room, let alone a house. You don't own a stick of furniture, or even a wooden bowl and spoon such as pilgrims and paupers carry on their persons. You're poorer than those to whom you gave your savings that day in Granada. Other men give the crust, you give the whole loaf." He did not look at John, but at the strong, supple fingers that caressed Our Lady's Rosary. "You thought of everything," said the priest with a sudden ring of despair in his voice, "except how to acquire the means to realize this ideal. God knows, if I had anything, I would put it at your disposal. But we both committed that which in the eyes of the world is folly. We gave away our all. My inheritance was considerable," he said frankly. "Had I but a fraction of it, I could provide you with a hospital. Neither of us attracts persons of wealth. Tramps and beggars dog your steps; solitaries dog mine. If they aren't poor to begin with, they cast off their wealth, as they cast off the world, for love of God."

"Other men have been poor and—" John began, then stopped, as the priest said, "They have, indeed. But I don't know of another who provoked abuse from a whole citizenry and let himself be driven off the streets with clubs and stones in order to suffer the cruelty accorded to madmen."

"It wasn't cruel enough," said John, soberly. "The harshest cruelty, the most burning humiliation that a man can receive from other men is a comfort compared to what Our Lord endured." John's shining eyes suddenly dimmed with pain.

There was silence between them.

"Do you think I am afraid to return to Granada?"

"Of course I don't think that. You don't know what fear is. But I'm convinced you don't know the hard side of human nature, either. Or, for that matter, the fear that besets worldly men. There isn't a merchant in Granada who'd give you a thing, nor one who would extend credit. They bolted their doors and drew the shutters over their stalls that day in January, believing you'd do them some grave mischief. They will do the same thing again. Beg a dish or a strip of linen, ask credit, and they will but mock you for the madman they still think you to be. Show them your letter of discharge with its curious statement that you were cured of a malady you never had, and they will revile you all over again." The whole thing was so improbable to John of Avila that he smiled in a tired, hopeless way. He waited for John to speak, but he remained silent. He merely gazed at the priest as if pleading with him to have faith in his plan.

With a pensive glance at John, the priest sighed again, then threw his arms wide in a helpless gesture. "What can I say!"

"What you will, Father. I promised always to do as you say."

"Yes," said the frantic priest, "but I don't want you acting on my advice when it means a pang that will cleave your heart in two. Heaven be my witness, the last thing I want is to be an impediment to good works. Yet one of us has to be reasonable. For your project, John, enthusiasm isn't enough, courage isn't enough, willingness to work isn't enough. You need money to establish and run a hospital, however small. Goodwill would help, but where's the Granadino who'll show you anything except suspicion? In time, your charity would overcome that attitude, but you lack the means with which to dispense charity. Your only legacy is a share in Christ's Passion. There is no greater. But will it buy, furnish and stock a hospital with necessary supplies?" The almost pitying look in John's eyes told the priest that he attached all importance to that legacy and scarcely any to the rest of the argument.

John of Avila's fingers drummed on the chair arms. "If you can think of a way to manage it, I'm more than willing to listen."

So John said mildly, yet with surety, "I can only say that this is what God asks of me, and that He wants what He wants. You are His voice for me, Father. It is for you to say what I shall do."

With a faint moan, the confessor leaned his cheek on his hand, resting his elbow on the leather arm of the chair. For a long moment he could only look at the eyes, deep-set in the thin face, lit up with a smile of extraordinary sweetness. Those eyes seemed to prompt him silently, as though to tell him, You know what to say. But he didn't. "If I could think how you might follow this through, I'd not only consent, I'd compel you to do it. To help people is the work that is cut out for you. In the circumstances, you cannot do it on your own. You've a quick mind and your strength is matchless. But the fact remains that you need more than brain and muscle."

"I have all that I need," John said simply.

"All?" Father John questioned in amazement. "Stowed away somewhere?"

"Yes, in a manner of speaking," the other replied, as he reached into the left sleeve of his tunic and withdrew from it a crucifix. "I have Him," he said. "What more do I need? Our Lord knows that I am homeless and without funds. Just the same, while being the poorest of the poor, He wishes me to look after other poor. It won't be easy. Mine isn't meant to be an easy life." He paused, pressed his lips against the nailed feet. "With His help," he said, after a second, "charity is possible, even for a nothing like me." Again he gazed down at the crucifix, while the priest gazed at him with the look of one who has seen a miracle.

The wintry wind whistled through the bare trees. John of Avila was about to speak when a crash of thunder stopped him. And then he felt too moved, too humbled by John's faith to say anything. Suddenly, the shaken priest stood up, and John stood up also. "Implore the assistance of Our Lady of Guadalupe," he said, in a tone which told John that he had his confessor's blessing. "And ask her to give you a sign."

"A sign?" cried John, disbelieving. "I don't need a sign. Nor could I ask one of her. She is the Mother of God, the Queen of Heaven," he said, as if John of Avila were not aware of it.

"She is your mother and your queen, too," the priest informed him, gently. "It pleases her to be appealed to."

"I appeal to her constantly, Father, but not for signs.

No, that I cannot do." Amazed at the suggestion, John wondered to himself, Why would he ask such a thing of me?
Why, indeed! Father John of Avila was one of the most
persuasive preachers in Europe. Having wanted to go to
Mexico as a missionary, he had been prevailed upon by
the Archbishop of Seville to use his oratorical genius on
his own countrymen in southern Spain, and for his powerful revival of the faith there became known as the Apostle
of Andalusia. His impressive sermons, for which his only
preparation was a four-hour meditation, recovered lost
faith and fanned to exceptional fervor that of lukewarm
Christians. Aware of these things, John became more and
more incredulous.

"A great preacher like yourself," he said, as he put his
crucifix back into his sleeve, "you would have inspired
words for the Blessed Virgin. You are learned as well as
holy. But I!" He shook his head vehemently. "I have no
words worthy of Our Lady."

"Oh, I think she would understand you, and I have a
feeling she would grant you any favor." The priest's calm
eyes looked up at John with an expression that the humble
penitent did not recognize as reverence. He recognized
nothing just now except a shrinking within himself. "Never
mind," said Father John quietly. "Since the very thought
turns you white, I withdraw my request." He smiled when
he saw the dismay on John's face give way to a relieved
expression.

"I'm curious, Father. If you do not object, will you tell
me what you had in mind? I mean," John questioned with
slow emphasis, "if I were able to ask for a sign, which I
am not, and if one were given, which would be most unlikely, what would you look for in it?"

"Your future," answered the priest.

"But why? Doing what I can for the needy in Granada, that is my future." With characteristic simplicity, John did not understand why that wasn't enough. He thought of himself as the lowliest instrument at God's disposal, and was thankful beyond words for the privilege of spending himself in the interests of persons as poor as himself, though not as healthy and strong.

"Charity takes many forms," argued the priest. "You cannot embrace them all. During your time in Granada, when you kept a stall, you seldom left the shadow of the Elvira Gate. Wait until you have a look around, a close look. For almost half a century, ever since the Siege of Granada, when all but a few of the Moors were defeated and driven out, the city of palaces and gardens has become the haunt for indigents, idlers, tramps and criminals. They go there from every kingdom in Spain. Why? Who knows!" Father John lifted his shoulders in a typically Spanish gesture. "Possibly because something invariably happens to a city that is lashed by battle. There was glory in victory for Ferdinand and Isabella, but loss as well. The Moors gave Granada much of its architectural beauty, its incomparable gardens and fountains; the Jews gave it wealth. There is about it now a kind of remote desolation that appears to encourage inertia. Pride prevents the hungriest beggar from bowing to the yoke of work; many are too proud to beg. You'll doubtless draw the poor to yourself in swarms. They will go to you with their afflictions and problems because you have a veritable talent for reassuring others that they are not alone, that you share their faults as well as their difficulties. Few men, John, are the separate individual that you are. And yet, you are sincerely able to identify yourself with anyone. You had young Andrés eating out of your hand," he recalled with a smile, "simply because you proved yourself human, a human being who finds it a trial to do without sleep."

All this while, John did not speak a word. He listened attentively, undismayed, perfectly serene.

"You see why I worry about you?"

The question was met with a smile. "There's no need to worry," John assured him.

"No need!" echoed the priest. "If you were sensible, I might agree. But when human wretchedness confronts you, you lose sight of all else. Once you stumble upon the blind and the crippled, foundlings, orphans, widows without means, young girls without families, all the unwanted and unloved that inhabit Granada, you will see it as your duty to protect them, every one. Now it is the sick poor alone that concern you. Before long, however, you will want to take the whole suffering population in your arms. You'll work yourself to death in order to gratify their wants and needs. I thought that perhaps a sign to indicate a specific work—" John of Avila stopped, left the sentence dangling. None knew better than he that God can wish the impossible and, with His grace, the one chosen for the work can accomplish it. Deep within him, too, was the realization that, while John of God listened with his usual respect, the words of admonition made no more impression on him than would a fistful of gravel flung at a crag. Overwhelmingly humble, John of God would be guided by Divine, not mortal reasoning, and he would surrender himself to the most arduous tasks, trusting with crystal simplicity in God's help.

The priest managed a rueful smile. "Even without eloquent phrases," he said to his penitent, "make an offering of yourself and your future work to Our Lady of Guadalupe. If your mind goes blank," he continued, trying for lightness, "that won't distress her. She will accept your blankness as an act of love, if you make it that. In any case, the pilgrimage will do you good." He paused, unable to dislodge a small worry from his mind. "My sole objection," he said, "is the season."

"Autumn?" John laughed gently. "That's nothing to fret about. Spring or autumn, what difference?"

"In your case, a big difference." Anxiously, John of Avila glanced at the other's slim bare feet on the blue floor tiles; then his gaze traveled the length of the tunic, all the way up to the bare head with its close-cut hair that seemed painted over the finely modeled skull by a heavy brush dipped in jet. "It's useless." He sighed. "Nevertheless, I do fret about you. There is no warmth in that tunic, it's nothing but cotton and flax. You refused the wool cloak I offered you when you first came, and you shrink at the idea of being released from your vow never again to wear shoes."

"You know the reason for that," said John quietly. "Pray God I may never break it." He lowered his eyes, as though to conceal the stab of longing that he felt at the thought of the lovely Child ascending, disappearing, dimmed by the golden light that was not of the sun.

Nodding his head, the priest colored slightly. Yes, he knew the reason, and the knowledge rebuked him for having offered to free John of his promise. In His own way, God had spoken to John in a sun-spangled wood when He gave him the thought to remove his shoes and go barefoot in imitation of the ragged little wanderer who was the Child Jesus, even as ages ago God spoke to Moses, saying: *Put off the shoes from thy feet: for the place whereon thou standest is holy ground.*

For a long moment all was silence, except for the rustle

of trees and the lingering overtones of faraway thunder.

With the sound of the thunder, Father John's uneasiness returned. "You'll be running into storms all along the way, and the cold is more penetrating in Guadalupe than here. You'll be drenched and you'll freeze." Immediately he had spoken, he was contrite. "I'm sorry. I ought to know better. For you, discomforts are but stars in your heaven of penances." Looking up at the pure, still face, it seemed to him that John's head was encompassed by light as white as the soft glimmer of stars.

Suddenly, the grave expression softened. John eyed him with fondness. "Please do not worry. It is nothing to me to be out in all weather. I was a shepherd." He brooded a moment, staring down at the cold blue floor. "The Divine Shepherd had no place to lay His head," John said, meditatively, "but I, who am nothing, I will be taken in."

"Are you sure?"

"Certainly, Father."

"Who will take you in?"

"Farmfolk. Rustics are the kindest of people." He paused, added very quietly, "I have known their goodness, known it completely." With a pang of sadness that made him unconsciously clutch at his rosary, he thought of Oropesa, of his foster parents and Maria Paz whose delicate charm was a thing to touch the heart.

The priest understood and waited a moment before he spoke. "Let me give you a small purse."

"Money? What for?"

"To pay for the hospitality you will receive."

"Father, I never beg alms or hospitality. I pay."

"With what?"

"Usually, with a bundle of faggots. I gather them along the way. If someone buys them off me, then I give the money to my host. Otherwise, I pay with prayers and faggots."

"What if doors are slammed in your face?"

"Then they are, although I can't think they will be. That was never my experience in the past."

"In the past, you presented a quite different appearance. Not that you went about in shining garments, but at least you were a conventionally attired giant. Now you're a giant in fustian girt with rope. Head bare. Feet bare. Your height, your flesh pared down to the bone by penances, your garb may well arouse doubts and questions. Don't forget that the Castilian peasant has something of the gypsy in his make-up. He is changeable of mind and often superstitious. Other pilgrims don cloaks, carry long staffs and have cockleshells on their hats. These externals identify them and readily gain them food and lodging. You've no cloak nor rod nor scallop shell, that ancient emblem of the pilgrim. Who will believe you are going to Guadalupe?"

"I don't know," replied John, "and I cannot see that it matters. In the end, it is not what I wear that will determine whether I find shelter or not, but the mysterious will of God. As for cloak, staff and shell, what use are they?" Touching his rosary, he said, "Our Lady's beads are greater protection than any cloak."

For a while, neither spoke, John caressing his beads, the priest motionless, hands clasped together.

Finally, John of Avila said, "I have delayed you. I ought to have remembered that, when you decide to leave a place, you leave in a hurry." He smiled good-naturedly. "I'll keep you no longer. Send word to me if you can. Pilgrims are constantly journeying through Montilla, to or from Guadalupe. Later, when you return to Granada, let me know what you need. If there is anything I can give, I will gladly furnish it." He paused and said to himself, God's mercy on them if they don't take him in. The priest would have liked to throw himself at the feet of this humblest and most cherished penitent. But it was John who knelt to him.

Standing again, he kissed the other's outstretched hand.

"Good-by, John. God be with you."

"Good-by, Father. Don't worry. Just pray for me." A smile quivered on his lips and there was a shining in his eyes. He bit down on his lip and turned to go. At the threshold he hesitated. With typical impulsiveness, he went back to his friend and flung his arms about him. Then, without a word, he was gone. With the swiftness of wind itself, he went out into the piercing wind that blew against his face and body and moaned overhead like a thousand brooding doves.

# TWELVE

ONLY moments ago the setting sun was an
orb of flame that ignited the plain and village of Fonte-
Ovejuna with crimson reflections. But hardly had it dipped
below the horizon when, to the west, where there ought to
have been a rosy afterglow, there spread a somber blue-
blackness veined with greeny lightning flashes. And now
the wind screamed and the air trembled with thunder
that rumbled like a procession of oxcarts rolling over
cobbles on solid wooden wheels.

His short, stocky figure wrapped in a fleece-lined cloak,
the mayor of Fonte-Ovejuna hurried from his office in the
village jail to his modest house at the far opposite end of
the plaza. Don Tomás was afraid of storms, and this one
was very strange. First the radiant sunset, then the way
blackness came down over the west long before it ought
to have come; the suddenness of wind, lightning and thunder. He read an ill omen in it all. Trouble was coming. He
could feel it in his bones.

"I do not like this, I do not," he said aloud and clapped
his hand to his eyes to ward off flying twigs and dust. Soon,
thank goodness, he would be out of this storm, safe and
warm in his comfortable house. Scarcely had he thought
this, when he found himself pounding on the door. Thunder drowned out his banging with knocker and fists.
"Dolores, let me in," he shouted to his wife. There was

silence within. In a howl of rage and impatience, he called Rosalia, the servant. As if in mocking reply, the thunder became more and more deafening. Then a ripping gust of wind swung the door inward. A loud thud resounded as it hit the wall. All his strength was needed to close and bolt it. Panting and trembling, Don Tomás flung off his hat and cloak and hung them on a door peg.

He turned . . . and stared in disbelief. The low-ceilinged room was dark as a cave, except where the topaz flame of a candle flickered before an image of Our Lady of Sorrows. Not a single lamp had been lighted, nor even a floating wick in an earthen dish of oil. In the hearth, embers glittered like a scattering of fireflies among the ashes, that was all. On the hearthstone sat a wooden trough filled with risen bread dough. Why wasn't the bread being baked? Why wasn't the table laid? He sniffed, caught no whiff of garlic-seasoned meat. Apparently there was no supper, either. For a minute he was too befuddled to move or speak. He wondered, even, if he had walked into his own house. The Virgin of Sorrows reassured him. Having momentarily forgotten the storm as well as his wife, he suddenly remembered both.

"Dolores!" he called out, half in anger, half in fright.

"I am here, Tomás." A quiet voice, more troubled than his own, came from a corner of the room. She said nothing more to him, only went on murmuring *Ave Marias*.

Don Tomás lit a floating wick at the candle's fire, and then he saw his wife. As if hypnotized, she sat rigid in a rush-bottom chair. Only the rosary beads slipped slowly through her fingers and her lips moved in prayer. His bushy eyebrows drew together in a frown of displeasure. "What's come over you?" he asked harshly. "Praying, at this hour!"

She did not answer. Her gaze clung to her image of the Sorrowful Virgin. Instead of a gold or a ruby-red gown, the sad-faced little image was dressed in black velvet, and into her heart plunged the points of seven tiny, shining swords. Teardrops of glass glinted on her cheeks and her violet-blue eyes were raised to Heaven. A miniature rosary of coral and silver dripped over her folded hands.

"Stop staring at her and speak to me!" Don Tomás' voice was husky with anger. "Why are you crying?" The tears in his wife's eyes were real. "What has happened here? Where is Rosalia?"

"I was unpardonably cruel," murmured Doña Dolores. "Rosalia ran home."

"Is that all? You wouldn't know how to be cruel, but if you chided that goose of a girl, she deserved it." Relieved and disgusted in one, he threw his arms out in a helpless gesture. "Women!" he exclaimed. "One wonders sometimes why God robbed Adam of a rib to create the first woman." Don Tomás did not hear his wife say that it wasn't Rosalia to whom she had been cruel. He had stomped over to the hearth. He gave the burnt-out log a fierce kick with his booted foot, threw on another log and some faggots. When flames began to leap from the wood, he dragged a chair up close to his wife's and tried for calmness.

"Unpardonably cruel." He echoed her words. "You are good, Dolores. At times," he sighed, with a glance at her rosary, "boringly good." He saw her wince and thought, mistakenly, it was the unkind word he had used that hurt her. Awkwardly he patted her hand, saying, "I didn't really mean that."

"I wish you did, I wish it were true," she murmured faintly, stung with remorse again. Then slowly, as if the words were choking her, she continued, "Rosalia is not at fault for anything. My unkindness was not directed at her. The instant I closed the door on him, my conscience writhed like those flames in the hearth. I was wrong in sending him away. I knew it in my heart. Rosalia knew it too, so well, indeed, that it frightened her out of the house."

Bewildered, Don Tomás stared at his wife, who had lowered her head. Speaking loudly, as if she were several rooms away, he said, "I don't know what you're talking about. On whom did you close the door? Who disturbed your conscience?"

"A man," she replied, still not looking at Don Tomás. "He did not give his name and I did not ask it. There was something unusual about him. He was full of quietness. Very tall, thin and solemn. Neither old nor young. He was wearing a coarse fustian tunic. His head and feet were bare. But there was a majesty about him." She paused, looked intently at her beads of olive wood. "His eyes," she went on, "were deep and black and shone with a gentleness beyond any I have ever seen."

The mayor rubbed his blunt chin and shot a long glance at his wife. "The only wrong you've done," he said, his patience running out, "is to regret having denied the beggar food and lodging."

"He was not a beggar," she defended stubbornly.

"A pilgrim, then?"

"I don't know. I know only that he asked leave to sleep in the stall with the ass. He offered a bundle of faggots in payment. When I said we had faggots, he answered that he would gladly give a full day's work in exchange. There was something about him that set him apart, and once he had left, he seemed more present than when he was here.

Rosalia and I both sensed it." Doña Dolores drew a deep sigh. "It was that, I think, as much as my unkindness, that made her suddenly set the dough trough on the hearthstone and run home to her mother."

"Rubbish!" snapped the mayor, and knew that, without cause, he had become angry with the stranger—and frightened of him, too. "You listen to me, Dolores," he grumbled. "Get a hold on yourself while you still can. It occurs to me that you have looked the devil in the eye. He is more cunning than you, in your blind goodness, can see."

"The devil is not in that man," asserted Doña Dolores firmly. "He was thin as a reed from fasting, of that I am certain, and tenderness of a kind I cannot describe shone from the depths of his eyes."

"Don't try my patience further." Don Tomás set his lips. Agitated, he got to his feet and paced back and forth. All at once he looked at the bare table. "Whatever the reason for this thinness, I don't intend to become lean on fasting," he exclaimed indignantly. "I've had a hard day. I want my supper. I am hungry."

"*You* had a hard day!" Her eyes blazed at him. "That poor man looked as if he had come a long way—and the whole way—without rest or food. The hunger in his face—" She broke off, looked again at the candlelit statue of the Virgin. "His hunger was not for bread and stew," she whispered. Turning toward the little image, she said, "Longingly, steadily he looked at the Virgin's statue, so steadily that I almost thought his eyes would never draw away . . . and then—"

"And then what?" rasped out the mayor.

"Then he asked a second time if he might stay in the stall, and I turned him away, saying I could not give him leave until you came home."

Somewhat appeased, Don Tomás asked, "How long is it since he left?"

Hope passed across her face like a light. "Hardly more than an hour ago, if that. You couldn't miss him, Tomás. As I told you, he is exceptionally tall and thin. He had no cloak, shoes or hat, merely a tunic of fustian tied with a knotted rope. And, oh yes," she recalled eagerly, "he was carrying a bundle of faggots."

There was a short silence. Pleadingly, Doña Dolores looked at her husband. "In this storm," she said, "he can't have gone far. Try to find him, Tomás, please. Please, will you?"

"I certainly will not," he barked, avoiding her eyes. "Besides, it isn't necessary. I know his kind. Close one door in his face, he'll go knocking at another."

She shook her head sadly. "Twice he requested shelter from the storm, not here in the house, merely in the stall with the ass, and twice he was refused. He asked God's blessing on me and smiled a little. That was all." Winding her beads about her fingers, she added quietly, "He had dignity. He will not return of his own accord." Briefly, she lifted her eyes to her frowning husband. "Please, Tomás, please."

"Please, nothing! Asking me, the mayor, to go out into that wind and lightning to find a wandering stranger! Where is *your* dignity? Anyway, rest assured that he has tried another door."

She made a slight affirmative motion of her head. "He has," she said. "He tried every house on three sides of the plaza."

"You watched him?"

"Yes. No one took him in."

"No one at all?" Don Tomás' fear was greater than his

pity. This was uncomfortably puzzling. Poor they were, but the folk of Fonte-Ovejuna understood charity. It might be only a bed of straw and a meal of bread, soup and humble chickpeas, yet what they gave they gave generously. Numberless beggars and pilgrims en route to the shrine of the miraculous Virgin of Guadalupe could attest to the kindness of his people. If every family on the plaza had rejected this man, there was a reason. There must indeed be something about him that set him apart, something to be carefully avoided. Plainly enough, he had put a spell on Dolores and the girl, Rosalia. Theirs appeared to be the only two hearts that were touched. Don Tomás' round, brown face darkened with another possibility. He convinced himself that the unusual violence of wind, thunder and lightning was somehow linked with the stranger. Suddenly, he paused in his thinking, conscious of how quiet everything was. Could it mean the stranger had departed the village? Convinced of this too, he crossed himself and gave thanks to God.

He glanced at his wife, his eyes bright and triumphant. Good-naturedly he said, "I'm sorry I was gruff. Come now, get me some supper. We've cheese and wine and—" The rest of his sentence was lost in a crash of thunder. And then the rain came, not in slow, quivering drops but in rapid cascades of water that struck the clay-tile roof with a sharp, clacking sound, as of hailstones or hard-shelled nuts hitting, then bouncing off the tiles.

Don Tomás darted to the window to close and latch the indoor shutters. Unaware of himself, he remained rooted to the spot, while the rising force of the wind splattered his startled face with rain. He gripped the window bars to steady himself, less against the wind than against the shock of what he saw. He threw a cautious glance at his wife.

Fortunately, she sat with head bowed, as though she meditated, deaf to the raging storm. He knew that he should let go his hold on the rain-dripping bars, lock the wooden panels and nonchalantly tell his wife to bestir herself. But he kept on standing there and gaping, his face going pale. Were his eyes to be trusted? Was anyone else witness to what he was seeing? Thrice he crossed himself, drew the shutters together and purposely left them unlatched. He needed an excuse to look out of the window again.

Unnerved and shaken, he crossed the room to have a draw at the wineskin. He thought, What does one do in such circumstances? Mother of Mercy! This would be the one day that Father Valdez is absent. I wish he had waited until tomorrow to visit his brother. This is a matter for the priest. What'll we do, with the priest in a village ten leagues distant?

Just as he was about to put the spout of the wineskin to his lips, the shutters flew open with a bang. Lightning illuminated the whitewashed walls of the room. The floor shone with water. Roused now, Doña Dolores left her chair and hurried toward the window, but Don Tomás flung himself in front of her. "No, no, no, I'll close the shutters." His voice quivered like his heart. "Get out of the way or you'll be drenched."

A moment later, he was dashing to the door in answer to the pounding of six fists. "Señor *Alcalde!* Don Tomás!" And once again he barred his wife with his arm. "Let me open. Please, Dolores, go back to your chair," he said roughly. "This is not for you." Her only reply was to stare at him with widened eyes.

Two farmers and a shepherd were admitted. Sopping wet, they were wild-eyed and paler than the mayor. Teeth chattering, they could barely speak. "Don Tomás," said the shepherd, and looked furtively at Doña Dolores. "I don't know how—"

"Neither do I, Miguel. But I know why the three of you are here. I saw him, too." Self-consciously, he avoided his wife's searching eyes. She had not returned to her chair but confronted the group, determined to discover the reason for this sudden commotion. "Tomás, you hate being in storms," she said, well aware that he had as great a fear of thunder and lightning as a gypsy bullfighter had of black bulls. "You're putting on your hat and cloak. Why? Where are you going?"

"Across the street," he answered, as he pulled his wide-brimmed rustic's hat low over his eyes. Feeling her glance burning through him, he assured her casually, "It's nothing."

"Nothing! Is it for nothing that Miguel, Diego and Julián all but broke their knuckles beating on the door? Is it for nothing that you as well as they are as blanched as if you'd seen a dozen ghosts?"

"Not a dozen, Doña Dolores." Miguel shook his head and a little shower of raindrops plopped off his hat to the floor. "Only one," he said. "He is camping in our plaza."

Her dark eyes became darker still. "Tomás," she asked, "is it the stranger?"

"Yes."

"That is why you would not let me close the shutters or open the door?"

"Yes."

"He is out there in that freezing rain?"

Don Tomás nodded.

"That was minutes ago," exclaimed Doña Dolores. "How could you let him stay out there on a night like this? For

love of the Holy Virgin," she begged, "fetch him in. He must be wringing wet and terribly cold. He can dry himself at the hearth."

Don Tomás shot Miguel a sidelong glance that said, You tell her.

Miguel cleared his throat. "That's just it," he began, and got no farther.

"Just what?"

"He isn't wet and he isn't cold. A few minutes out there and we were drenched, and we have heavy clothing on. He's been in the plaza since the rain started; longer, maybe, I don't know. I can only tell you that the plaza is a lake, except where he is. He's sitting on ground as dry as the desert. He himself is as dry and warm as if the sun were

shining on him. Not a drop of rain has touched him, and
his fire burns on and on."

"His fire!" Doña Dolores gasped. "Miguel, you're dreaming."

"No, he isn't, señora," Julián assured her. "With our
own eyes we saw it. The fellow has a bundle of sticks at
his side. The faggots are wet as eels, yet for him wet wood
burns like a pile of dry leaves."

Stunned, she turned to her husband. "Did you also see
the fire burning in the rain?"

"Yes, I saw it. What's more, the flames burn straight;
they neither flutter nor lean with the wind."

"On your way over here, did you pass him?" Doña
Dolores asked of Miguel.

"We not only passed him, señora, we stood right behind
him. Did he know it?" Miguel shrugged. "If so, he took
no notice of us. He just sat there, tranquil as a shepherd
keeping the night watch."

"I wish you had asked his name."

"I shouldn't care to know his name, señora. It's best not
to get acquainted with one who has power over water and
fire. I daresay he could walk through flames and not be
burned. The man's a sorcerer."

"A sorcerer? That man?" Doña Dolores smiled. "Don't
be silly, Miguel. He came here asking for shelter. His is a
face as kind as Heaven."

"Your pardon, señora, but the man who stays dry in
rain and keeps a fire burning in it is a wizard of some
sort, and not a good sort."

"The man who can do that," she countered boldly, "has
God with him. He gave him protection because the rest
of us refused it. It's as simple as that."

There was a long silence. It was Miguel who finally broke

it. "There's something in what you say, señora. The man came to me for shelter. He said he'd be leaving at sunrise, that he is going to Guadalupe. I suppose he is a pilgrim. I could easily have taken him in. I don't know what made me close the door in his face. Later, I was sorry for it. When the rain came down in sheets, I went to the window in the hope of seeing him. It was my intention, if I saw him, to invite him in. Well, I saw him. There in the middle of the plaza, sitting before his fire." He glanced at his companions, saying, "It happened the same way with each of us. By now, everybody in Fonte-Ovejuna must be making an act of Contrition. Not for having rejected him," he explained, "but in the hope of being spared a curse."

"I tell you he is not an evil man," insisted Doña Dolores. "He'll do us no harm." Turning to her husband she asked, "What were you expecting to do with him?"

"I hadn't made up my mind. But we don't want him in our plaza."

"Still less in our houses," put in Diego.

"Can't you leave him where he is?" Doña Dolores appealed to her husband. "He's hurting no one," she reasoned quietly, "and he told Miguel he'll be leaving early in the morning."

"That he will, first thing in the morning, if not sooner. This is my problem, Dolores, not yours. If Father Valdez were here, the matter would be in his hands. He is away, so it's up to me."

"To do what?" she asked, fearfully.

"To get him out of Fonte-Ovejuna. The sooner the better."

Now it was Doña Dolores who went white and quivery. "May you be forgiven, all of you," she murmured, "if what you saw in the plaza is a miracle of God."

"Dolores!" Don Tomás could not have been more horrified had he heard an oath fall from the lips of his pious wife. "Don't confuse a miracle of God with a sorcerer's tricks," he said sternly.

"Don't you deal with him harshly," was all she replied.

"I have no wish to be harsh, simply just. I have the safety of the people to consider." He paused, then said impatiently, "Busy yourself with something. There is bread to be baked. Bake it."

"Tomás—"

"What now?"

"Let him remain until morning. Then—" She stopped, plucked at his cape. He removed her hand. "Then," she pleaded, "may he have a loaf? He is very poor."

"You *are* bewitched! He'll get no loaf from you or from me. I've heard enough. Come on, let's go," he said to the three men.

"Don Tomás—" Miguel groped for words. "To an extent, I think Doña Dolores is right. Look at it this way: if he is a sorcerer, giving him a loaf of bread would not make any great difference, one way or another. If he is a God-fearing Christian, surely God will take note of our charity. I am willing to add an alms to the loaf."

Before the mayor could answer him, his attention was arrested by a din that rose above the storm's blast. It resembled the sound of a turbulent river roaring through a steep-sided canyon. But it wasn't a river. It was the howling of an angry mob of villagers. The voices rose and fell, rose again, came closer and closer to the mayor's door.

"We'd better go," Don Tomás said with authority. "Keep away from the window," he ordered his wife.

"I will, I will, only don't let them hurt him. You can

prevent violence. Suppose," said Doña Dolores desperately, "suppose he is a holy man, a saint. Tomás, don't raise your hand against him, please don't."

"You do as I say," he shot back. "I'll do as I think best."

# THIRTEEN

SERENE and clothed in stillness, John of God sat in the dry center of the water-streaming plaza as on a little island in the midst of a wind-wrinkled lake. To the shuddering accompaniment of thunder and drumming rain, he told his beads.

For a long moment, Don Tomás and his village men stood staring at him. Cautiously they kept a certain distance from the bone-dry stranger and the straight-burning flames. Uneasily conscious of the many eyes that silently challenged him to speak, Don Tomás demanded, "You, there, what are you doing?"

Over John's lips ran the faintest of smiles. Holding up his string of black beads, he replied simply, "I am saying Our Lady's rosary. I have always found it very helpful."

"The question wants a better answer than that," boomed Isidro, the goatherd.

John looked down at his beads; then his dark, shining eyes met the sneer on Isidro's face. "I see. I didn't understand, at first. I came but this afternoon to Fonte-Ovejuna. I did not know where else to go, so I came here," he said, not wanting to say that he had received a slight from every man of them. "If I am not in anyone's way," he added, "I will be grateful for permission to stay the night."

"I'm not the one to give it, that's up to the *alcalde*," Isidro said sourly, and gestured toward Don Tomás. "But if I'd anything to say about it—" He broke off, seeing the scowl on Don Tomás' face.

John's eyes searched the mayor's face. "Would you prefer that I leave at once, señor?"

"Well," said Don Tomás uncertainly, and fingered his chin.

"Well, what? Are you afraid to speak plainly?" Isidro burst out, unafraid of the mayor but full of fear of the stranger who regarded him without bitterness. "Are you blind, Don Tomás? Can't you see that he's too placid, too humble to be trusted?"

For the moment, Don Tomás saw only a haunting sadness about John's eyes.

"Answer him, Don Tomás. Tell him to get himself out of our village."

"Be still, Isidro," the mayor ordered, frowning. He took a step closer to John. "Who are you?" he asked him.

As he looked up into the brown eyes, John answered, "I am nobody."

"A man without a name?"

"My name is John."

Don Tomás stood stock-still, gazing now at the flames, now at their reflection in the hollows of John's face. "Well, then, what are you?"

"I am nothing," John replied quietly.

"Have you no trade?"

"I have had many."

"The devil has many trades, too," spoke up a friend of Isidro. "Apart from that," called out another, "the devil can disguise himself in human form." The meaning was not lost. It sent a tremor over the peasants.

Miguel moved closer to the mayor and nudged his arm. "Ask him where he comes from."

In reply, John said, "I was born in Portugal."

"That tells us nothing."

"I'm sorry, señor. I was thinking of something." John's solemn face revealed itself suddenly as that of a man who has suffered. With a catch in his voice, he said, "For all but the first nine years of my life I have lived in Spain."

"Where in Spain?"

"Oropesa—" he began, and was interrupted by Don Tomás, who said, "Ah!" and nodded as if in approval. "Oropesa is not very far from here, and nearer yet to Guadalupe."

"True enough," someone observed, "but I saw him when he entered Fonte-Ovejuna and he came from the opposite direction."

"That is right. I came from Montilla." John did not glance at the speaker. He only smiled reflectively, his thoughts on Father John of Avila.

"Is Montilla your village?"

"No, señor. I go wherever God leads me. Oropesa, Seville, Gibraltar, Granada." He paused. "I am on my way to the shrine at Guadalupe."

"So are thousands of others. You still haven't said where your home is."

"I have no home."

"And your family?"

"I have no family. No one." John took up the last sticks in his bundle of faggots and placed them crosswise, one over the other, on the fire. A trail of smoke, blue as dusk, drifted upward through rain that in the lightning glittered like splintered crystal. Steadfastly, he held his gaze on the flames.

The mayor looked from John to Miguel and then back again, and a crease of worry appeared between his brows.

Silently, he admitted that he could like this odd man if he let himself; then again, he thought, it was not impossible that Isidro, spiteful though he was, rightly sensed the peril the stranger personified. Don Tomás coughed dryly. Lifting his voice, he demanded, "You, whoever you may be, are you christened?"

John's pensive face broke into a smile. "Yes, señor, I am."

"Ask him how he stays dry in the rain, while the rest of us are drenched to the skin." Isidro's shrill demands started again. "Ask him how he makes wet faggots burn and keeps them burning in a storm. Ask him!"

But before Don Tomás could open his mouth, John looked up from the flames whose reflected radiance enveloped him as in a roseate cloud and spoke calmly. "What you see, señores, is not of my doing. The answer lies in the goodness and greatness of God."

There was silence.

"Perhaps Doña Dolores was right. Perhaps he is a holy rather than an evil man." Miguel's words pierced the hush and seared John's soul like fire. He flinched as at the sting of burning coals when Miguel added, "Would God prove His power in this fashion toward any but a holy man?"

"For saying such a thing," retorted Isidro, "Father Valdez would give you a week's penance. What's more, if he were here, he would force the truth from him. Maybe," he taunted John, "you don't know what happens to heretics and sorcerers?"

John didn't know, nor was he disturbed by the threat, only by the idea of being thought holy.

"It might go easier with you if you'd own up to what you are," shouted Isidro, as he pushed his way through the crowd and swaggered up to John.

"I told you what I am. I am nothing."

"You're a sorcerer." Isidro glared at him. "Admit it, admit it!"

"God forgive you, brother. Oh, not for what you've said about me, but for your lack of faith in the infinite power and goodness of God. In His mercy, Our Lord has spared you, all of you, the bother of taking me in and has bothered Himself instead to shelter me from the storm."

"Liar! Sorcerer! You—" Isidro could say no more. He could not get John's sad, penetrating black eyes out of his mind. The patient, uncondemning way in which they looked at him made him fidget and forget what he'd intended to say. John's slow smile had a similar effect on him. "You must be what I said," Isidro exclaimed in a voice that quavered now, "you—you must be or you'd not smile at such a charge." Shamed and frightened by what he knew deep down must be extraordinary goodness, he backed off from John, then dove through the mob into the darkness beyond.

"Do you also take me for a sorcerer?" John asked the mayor. His tone, curiously hopeful, was more disconcerting to the other than the burden of the question. Don Tomás stared woodenly, replied nothing.

"Señor—" Miguel took a deep breath, came closer to John and said firmly, "the accusation is a serious one, yet it appears not to upset you." He hesitated, then rushed on, "If anything, you look—pleased."

"How long must we wait? When are you going to act?" a farmer on the edge of the crowd demanded of the mayor.

"Antonio is right. Put an end to this business. Do we want a sorcerer in our village?"

Fists and shouts of "No!" went up together.

The open hostility of the villagers did not trouble John.

He welcomed their ill treatment. But he felt sorry for the faltering mayor and recognized the dilemma he was in. Unexpectedly, he said to him, "If you share the belief of your townsmen, turn me over to the Grand Inquisitor." To the horrified face turned toward him, John did not explain that this notion came to him when his mind raced back to Father John of Avila. The great confessor himself had been brought to trial before the Holy Office, though not on charges of sorcery. John of Avila was accused of locking the gates of Heaven to the miserly rich. But as promptly as he was examined, he was declared innocent and released.

"He's no sorcerer," Miguel said to the lip-biting mayor. "I don't pretend to understand him, but that much is clear. Show me the sorcerer who'd suggest the Inquisition for himself!" Looking now at John, he asked, "Why do you encourage trouble for yourself? They," he jerked his head toward the waiting crowd of men, "will be only too glad to deliver you up to the Holy Office."

There was no immediate answer. John seemed in some faraway dream. He was thinking of his Saviour who, at the end of His short life, was dragged from one tribunal to another; endured the irresoluteness of Pontius Pilate, the hatred of Caiaphas, the ultimate, inevitable sentence of death by crucifixion.

"Listen to me, señor, please." Miguel was oddly concerned about this stranger. "Show some will to prove your innocence. Fight, if only with words."

"Our Lord did not fight," John reminded him. "He did not defend Himself. Who am I to ask kindness of anyone?"

The stranger neither asked nor received it. A moment later, stones, sticks and mud came flying at him. It was not without great effort that Don Tomás brought his villagers under control. "Have done, the lot of you! Go home!"

"Not until we know where he's going. Hurry up, Don Tomás, make up your mind what to do with him, or we'll do it for you. Don't fool yourself, he has something up his sleeve."

"My brother has spoken truly." John smiled.

"I'm brother to no sorcerer," the speaker lashed out at him.

John did not say anything, but he achieved a breathless effect when he drew his crucifix from his sleeve, kissed the pierced feet and then replaced it.

"I knew it, I knew it! Black devil!" yelled the one called Guido. "He put it back upside down. That's enough to tell us what he is."

"Silence!" commanded Don Tomás. "Is it," he asked John, "is it upside down?" To the superstitious, a crucifix placed in this wise was considered a dire omen.

"See for yourself, brother." John extended his arm.

But the mayor would not. "You look," he said to Miguel.

Necks craned, all eyes were on Miguel. "It is not upside down," he announced. "It could not be held that way," he told them "for the arms of the cross are fixed in place by a small strip of cloth sewed to the inside of the sleeve."

"No matter," Guido shouted. "Get on with your duty, Don Tomás. Throw him out!"

There was an earsplitting chorus. "Throw him out! Run him out of Fonte-Ovejuna!"

Mingled with his curiosity about this man who offered no resistance was a growing respect for him which the mayor was afraid to show. Asserting his authority with a touch of bluster, he hushed the excited men. Then, with a harshness he did not feel, he said to John, "Get up. Come with me."

The peasants gaped at the supremely dignified figure John cut when he got to his feet. In the main, thickset and short-statured themselves, they gazed at his leanness and height in dumb amazement. Lightning hurled its shining javelins, thunder rumbled without cease, but the rustics of Fonte-Ovejuna were unaware of everything except the black-eyed man of quiet intensity. Tall and straight he stood, like a statue mysteriously imbued with breath—and with light. A radiance that was not of the fire came from him, or surrounded him; they could not have said which. Stricken silent, they were, if anything, more uneasy in his presence than before. One after the other twisted himself out of the crowd and hurried home.

John shook his head. "Señor," he said to the mayor, his voice all earnest apology, "I'd never have stopped in your plaza had I dreamed my being here would create such a disturbance. I am truly sorry. Now that the plaza is empty once more, please do not let me give you further trouble."

Don Tomás wiped rain from his eyes with the back of an equally wet hand, and seemed almost afraid to look up at the pallid ivory of John's face, untouched by the downpour. He was afraid, too, to glance at the fire that still burned. "What do you mean?" he demanded suddenly. "Surely you are not suggesting that I allow you to spend the rest of the night here in the plaza?"

"Why not, señor?" John queried with mildness.

"I cannot well have a war in my village, that is why not. No, you'll stay in the jail."

John nodded patiently. "Whatever you will, señor."

So Don Tomás' hard, stubby fingers gripped John's right arm and Miguel lightly took hold of his left, while Diego and Julián, grimly bringing up the rear, went with them, the five splashing through watery mire to the jail.

Once there, Don Tomás plucked a huge iron key from among others that jangled on the ring at his broad leather belt. The key grated in the lock; the heavy door screeched open on an airless, damp, foul-smelling cell.

The mayor spoke bruskly. "Go in," he said and followed John, remaining just inside the threshold, while his three silent companions stood at his back. For an overlong moment, Don Tomás contemplated his prisoner, impressed, in spite of himself, by his docile, uncomplaining manner, not knowing that obedience was second nature to John. As striking as his looks, the mayor was thinking, was this man's lack of fear. He was afraid of no one. Don Tomás' chin dropped in thought. Should he release him from this wretched cubicle and lodge him in his house? For that matter, the ass's stall was a thousand times preferable to this cell. What had the man done to deserve the worst the village could offer? He was guilty of no wrong. He had not robbed or harmed a soul, nor even asked for food, but merely for shelter from the storm, and that with the farm beasts in a stall, shed or cote.

Ever quick to sense struggle in another, whether the strain was bodily or mental, John's black eyes caught the other's. "Is there something, señor?" he asked gently.

"No, nothing." Don Tomás' lips tightened, as if to keep the admiration that he felt for John from escaping in a friendly word. He appeased his conscience somewhat by reasoning that this odd person, who had told them he was nobody, looked upon himself as nothing, claimed to have neither home, family nor trade (apparently he worked at whatever came along, if he worked at all), might well turn out to be a dangerous character. Don Tomás gazed down at the mud-colored floor of hard-packed earth over which cockroaches shuttled back and forth. "All right," he muttered offhandedly, "you can sleep here if you want to."

John gave him his slow, sad smile. "Thank you, brother," he said.

Don Tomás flushed a dark red. Eyes still lowered, he said, "We will free you at daybreak. You shall have bread. Then go your way and don't come here again."

"Yes, señor." John's hand hesitantly touched the other's shoulder. "Do not be afraid," he said. "I will do exactly as you say."

With a curt nod, Don Tomás went out, then locked the door.

As the mayor and his three friends left the jailhouse, the night's sudden stillness took them unawares. They paused, glanced about them as at a miracle. The storm had ended. Hushed were the mingled voices of wind, rain and thunder. The only sound was of water flowing over cobbles in sloping streams that mirrored the rays of a cold white moon. Above, stars pulsated against the sky's blackness with a diamond blaze that seemed to dim, then kindle again, like myriad votive lights flickering in some vast shrine.

"It's all over," said Miguel. He lifted his hand toward the plaza. "His fire died out."

The others nodded wordlessly.

At last they stirred from the shadows and walked along in the moonlight, under dripping trees.

Miguel looked at the mayor and said dryly, "He certainly didn't give much trouble."

"He didn't give any. I'd feel happier if he had been difficult. Nothing outraged him, not even being locked up in the jail."

"From first to last," put in Diego, "he was like a statue of patience."

"And sorrow," said Julián. "But his sorrow isn't for himself, you can see that. Now when it is too late, I would help him if I could."

"I could be his friend, too," Don Tomás admitted. "I wanted to take him to my house. I hated to leave him in that roach-infested hole."

"Why did you?"

Don Tomás slanted a look at Miguel for the terse question. "I had to. I am the mayor. I have to consider my position."

"Oh," said Miguel, and thought, That is how it was with Pontius Pilate.

"If you've anything to say to me, say it, Miguel. I don't like insinuation."

"There is nothing to say, señor. What's done is done. It was for you to do as you judged best. If you only knew what is best!"

"In other words, I didn't do the right thing?"

"I don't know, señor, truly I don't know."

"Forget about him," Diego advised.

"Forget! He is not easily erased from the mind."

"Well, morning will come."

"You're more optimistic than I am, Julián. Feeling ran high tonight," said Don Tomás. "It subsided, yes, but in the morning it will flare up again. Isidro, Guido and all the rest will be on hand to see him off. It won't be a quiet leave-taking. I'll do what I can, but I can't clear the village of every stone and stick."

None spoke for some moments. There was no sound but their footsteps and the flowing away of rainwater.

"Who is he?" Don Tomás began again. "That is what I would like to know. John—there are as many Johns in Spain as there are stars overhead."

Diego shrugged his shoulders. "What matter, señor? After sunrise, we will have seen the last of him."

"You think so?"

Diego's voice was low. "Yes, señor. Who wouldn't think so, in view of what you said to him? *Then go your way and don't come here again.* The man has dignity, as well as patience and grief."

"Dignity," echoed Don Tomás. "That's what my wife said of him, too."

Miguel sighed, spoke as to himself in a tone that was scarcely audible. "Claudia—Claudia Procula. That was her name."

"Who's name?" Don Tomás asked him.

"A woman not unlike Doña Dolores."

Don Tomás looked at him in surprise, unaware that Claudia Procula was the wife of Pontius Pilate.

"Well," said Miguel, as they reached the mayor's door, "at sunup we give him to the rabble."

# FOURTEEN

ON a day of sunshine and biting wind that swept the flower-blue sky bare of clouds, Miguel opened his door to the rapping of two pilgrims.

"Goyo! Ruben! God save you! You're shivering like castanets. Come in. It's good to see you. But I didn't expect to hear your staffs pounding on my door so soon again. Have you nowhere else to go?" teased the shepherd, as he drew up chairs for them at a table near the hearth. "Why, it seems no time since I laid on my stoutest log to warm you and filled your bowls with stew. No stew today. It's Friday. Sit down, sit down. Will bread, cheese and goat's milk do?"

They did not answer.

"Yes or no? I've nothing else to offer. What there is, you're welcome to." Miguel's honest hazel eyes searched the two familiar faces. His own became as grave as theirs. "What's wrong?" he asked.

Rubbing one hand over the other at the red and yellow glow of the wood fire, Goyo shook his head. "We don't know. We're wondering. It was our intention to spare you this time and beg a moment's warmth and a crust from another. But—"

"I don't understand," Miguel said.

"Miguel, either Fonte-Ovejuna has been abandoned or the folk behind the doors we knocked on pretended not to be at home. No one opened to us, no one," Goyo told him, incredulous. "Until today, a pilgrim could always count on a welcome in this village." He was quiet for a moment. "We arrived with five other pilgrims. They were going to try Don Tomás' door. How did they fare? We didn't wait to find out."

In thoughtful silence, Miguel fetched a jug of milk, bowls and bread. Absently he said, "Share the loaf between you. It is fresh baked. I will give you another for your homeward journey."

"God reward you, Miguel." Ruben tore off a chunk of the crusty, coarse-grained bread and ate hungrily. "Would that all men were as good as you. When we go again to Guadalupe, why not join us? You have never been. You're single. What's to keep you?"

"Sheep and goats. They can't be left alone and they can't be taken along."

Goyo smiled. "Our Lady wouldn't mind if you brought your flocks. Who can question her love for shepherds?" Dipping a piece of bread into his bowlful of milk, he continued, "Centuries ago, it was a shepherd she favored when she directed that the image which we venerate today be recovered from its hiding place."

"I know. I've thought of him more than once when I've struggled with the hard soil here. It is a thing to ponder," said Miguel, "how that shepherd felt when, right out of the blue, the Blessed Virgin approached him and said, 'Dig there and you will find a treasure. Then let it be known that on this mountain summit I wish to have a chapel built.' Digging with his bare fists in the stony earth of the mountain was work, real work. Imagine his feelings when he found nothing more remarkable than a bell. A simple youth, he didn't know that the priceless thing he sought had once belonged to Pope St. Gregory the Great, and that when the Moors invaded our land this small object was buried, for safekeeping, where the great shrine now stands. Ah, but when he lifted the bell, there it was! The miraculous image of the Virgin of Guadalupe." Miguel paused before going on in a reminiscent tone. "My father, who was also a shepherd, made the pilgrimage to her coronation. She was crowned the very same day that Columbus discovered America. King Don Ferdinand and the Cardinal Primate of Spain placed the precious crown on the head of the little statue, and then the Cardinal's voice rang through the church like a great wind blowing. 'The Virgin of Guadalupe is our Mother!' he called out. 'The Virgin of Guadalupe is our Queen!' "

For a long moment Miguel was still. Suddenly he noticed that Goyo and Ruben were leaning forward, intently, and not eating. He apologized. "Forgive me," he said, "for putting memories before courtesy, and for doing all the talking. Worse yet," he smiled, "I expect I was talking more to myself than to you. Shepherds fall into that habit. We are much alone. Come, have more bread," he urged. "Milk? Cheese? You have had more than you wanted? Impossible!" He laughed softly. "Vaya, then tell me about your pilgrimage. Tell me all. I can see that something is burning to be said."

"Something is, indeed," Goyo began, his brown face glowing. Quickly he took a swallow of milk against the sudden dryness in his throat. "Miguel, we saw a saint." The wonder in Goyo's voice was reflected in his eyes— but it was not in Miguel's. Slightly offended by the other's complacency, Goyo demanded, "Do you doubt it?"

"What a question! Of course I don't, Gregorio." Miguel used his friend's given name as if to add emphasis to his reply. "But I am not surprised. You aren't the first to say he has seen a saint at Guadalupe. It's the rare pilgrim who comes through here and doesn't make that announcement. Believe me, I am convinced that day in, day out, the monastery church is filled with saints, if one but knew them."

"You're generalizing, Miguel. I refer to a particular saint, and there's no one at Guadalupe who doesn't know him, at least by sight."

Ruben chimed in, "Not to notice him would be impossible."

"Why? What distinguishes him from other men?"

"Everything."

"Now who's generalizing!"

"He is not easily described." Ruben fell silent. Finally, he said, "A great man should look great. A saint should look a saint. Vaya, this one has the look of both. He's as tall and thin as the stone saints that smile down gravely from above the doors of Gothic cathedrals. There is a certain radiance about him. It is always evident, but most noticeable when he is at prayer. He is the poorest, humblest man I ever saw—also the saddest and most joyful." Ruben paused, caught up his long rosary that dripped black beads from his waist cord to the floor. "I can't do him justice," he declared.

"Neither can I," said Goyo. "I just can't tell you. But all the love and devotion there is seems to be gathered together in his person. His appearance and his piety are so remarkable that you would have to see him to understand."

Miguel wasn't too sure that he hadn't. He glanced from one to the other in a strange way, which they again took to mean disbelief. Ruben raised his rosary crucifix, saying,

"By the three nails and the wood of the cross of Jesus, it is the truth. The saint saw Our Lady."

"Doesn't every pilgrim see her?" Miguel tried to sound casual.

"All see the sacred image, yes. We aren't speaking of the image. The Most Pure herself appeared to this one, and the Holy Babe was with her."

Miguel gasped. "An apparition? A real one? While you were there? You saw it?"

"To your first three questions, yes; to the last, no. We were resting in the pilgrims' hospice when it happened. But the Prior of the Hermits of Saint Jerome was present. He witnessed it from beginning to end. Later, he gathered us all together and described the apparition for us. However, he forbade us to mention it among ourselves or to newcomers. We had to act as though nothing extraordinary had occurred."

"Why was that?"

"Because," Goyo told him, "he wished to edify us. At the same time, the saint's humility made silence essential. The Prior said that, if the saint discovered the fact that the pilgrims knew of the apparition, he would disappear."

"You still are pledged to silence?"

"Oh, no." Goyo smiled. "There's no concealing it beyond the precincts of the monastery. Word of the miracle and apparition will spread like brush fire."

"Miracle and apparition," Miguel repeated dazedly, saying the words and missing the difference. He thought them one and the same. "Please, Goyo, tell me what the Prior told you."

"Gladly. First, though, you must know that the saint prayed endlessly before the hallowed image. Whether the church was filled or empty, he was on his knees before Our

Lady's altar. Sometimes he seemed to be in a trance, he was so quiet; at other times, his rich, low voice resounded through the shrine. Desperately, yes, desperately, he implored the Mother of God to show him what her Divine Son wanted him to do with his life. Then one day she answered his appeal." Goyo stopped, took another sip of milk.

The small room was utterly silent, save for the snip-snap of the burning logs.

"Come, friend, say on."

"Well, while the saint fervently persisted in this prayer, a cloud drifted down upon the altar of the Virgin of Guadalupe."

"A cloud?"

"Yes, a cloud such as the wind shapes, the kind one sees in the sky, except," said Ruben, who had taken up the account, "it wasn't white or gray but of a dim blue color, like the blue of incense fumes. Sparkling through the misty blueness were a crown of gold and a small golden halo with a cross on it. Little by little, the blue vapor dissolved and there, more radiant than sunlight, stood the Most Blessed Virgin with the Holy Infant on her arm. All the rare gems, all the priceless gowns embroidered by princesses and queens for the doll-like image of the Guadalupe were as pebbles and sackcloth compared to the luster of Our Lady's robe and mantle. From her cincture fell a rosary, a chain longer than mine, of crystal, clear as sunlit dew. She smiled at the saint. Overcome, he buried his face in his hands."

Miguel said, "Did Our Lady speak?"

"No, she merely waited for him to raise his eyes to hers. At length he looked up. His face, the Prior said, became pale as marble, then brightened with that strange glow

which is peculiarly his, when the Blessed Virgin moved a
step closer to him. She leaned forward and held out the
Child to the saint. He rose from his knees. He lifted his
hands, then let them fall at his sides, as though he could
not believe that it was for him to touch the Child. With
an understanding smile, the Holy Mother herself put the
Infant in his arms. Mutely adoring Him, he knelt again.
Tears ran down his cheeks as he cradled the Baby in his
arms. He said something. The Prior was not certain, but
he thought he heard him say, 'The poor little Baby is cold.
He should have warmer clothing.' It was then that the
Blessed Mother let drift to the saint's shoulder a robe, like
a christening dress, and a small cloak of white velvet, the
Prior thinks it was, all a-gleam with tiny jewels the color
of pomegranate seeds."

"That meant—?" Miguel drew a deep breath and shook
his head, unable to say more.

"It meant," said Goyo, "that the saint was to dress the
Holy Babe. He understood. Enraptured, he clothed Him,
arranged every fold and pleat, smoothed out the sleeves,
wrapped Him in the little mantle, then held the Divine
Head to his breast in a very spasm of joy. At last he stood
and returned Him to His Mother, upon whom the Infant
smiled as if at the white fire of a star. There was an instant of dazzle, a light too glitteringly bright to see through.
That was all. Once more the altar was in shadow, with
only the flame in a silver vigil lamp throwing a pale shimmer over the diminutive Virgin of Guadalupe."

The shepherd fidgeted with the lacings of his leather
smock. Abruptly he left his chair and needlessly threw
more wood on the fire. "You say he is tall and thin?"

"Very."

"What color are his eyes?"

"Black—wide and deep set."

Reflectively, Miguel drew his hand across his chin and stared at the smoke that curled and fumed over the fresh log. "Narrow-shouldered?" he asked, without looking at the pilgrims.

"Narrow!" Goyo laughed. "He could easily carry a man over each. Why?"

"Nothing, just wondering." To himself Miguel said, *the description fits. Still, twenty-seven days have passed since that night.* "When did the apparition take place?" He put the question matter-of-factly.

"Last week," said Ruben.

"How long were you there?"

"Three days. One may go as often as one pleases, but each visit has to be limited to three days. Otherwise, the monks cannot accommodate the continuous flow of pilgrims."

"I see." Miguel's sense of relief was short, for, just then, Goyo said, "Naturally, the saint is an exception. He'd hardly arrived when the Prior removed him from the hospice to the monastery. He had been there fully three weeks at the time that we left."

Miguel could feel himself going pale. "Who is the saint, or don't you know?"

Together they answered, "His name is John."

In a sudden flurry of excitement, Miguel flung on his long brown shepherd's cloak, saying all in a breath, "You'll find cheese over there, olives, some cold chickpeas. Help yourselves. I have to see the mayor. Don't leave. I'll be right back."

# FIFTEEN

GOYO was about to ask, Is something wrong? but the question was superfluous. Miguel had blown in again in more of a state than when he had blown out.

"God help us!" He moaned faintly. "We used him shamefully, called him a sorcerer, threw him into jail overnight. At daybreak, we ran him out. I am no less guilty than the ones who flung mud and sticks and stones at him. I could have tried to help him. Oh, I wouldn't have succeeded, but I ought to have tried, and I ought to have taken him in. Every last one of us turned a saint from our doors. That wasn't enough," Miguel continued bitterly. "We had to hound him out of the village. He made no attempt to escape the torment we gave him. Not a word did he say, except to thank us." With a quivering hand, Miguel tugged at his neck chain and looked at the medal of the Virgin of Guadalupe that hung from it. He kissed it, then shut his eyes for a moment.

"We'll go now," Ruben said quietly.

Miguel's closed eyes flew open. "No, no, don't go! I have something to tell you." There was that in his tone which made Ruben ask excitedly, "Is the saint here?"

"No, I wish he were. That we'll not see him again is a penalty we deserve." Gloomily, Miguel stared through a small window. The wind was blowing up clouds of flaxen dust. Where there was stubble, sheep were grazing, and here and there a conical heap of gray-lavender rock looked like a dimmed amethyst in a pale-yellowish setting. "Nevertheless," Miguel said, bringing himself back to the moment, "the saint is in every mind, on every tongue. Everybody, almost, is at the mayor's house. I guess that is why no one opened to your knocking. Your five companions of the road are still there, as well as a shepherd who is headed for a cattle fair a few leagues away. There is such a great commotion, I could hardly distinguish one voice, one word from another."

"They've heard about the apparition?"

"That," said Miguel, "and two miracles."

"Two?" Goyo straightened with surprise. Turning to Ruben, he said, "There must have been another since the sacristan's leg." To Miguel, he remarked, "You know of that, of course."

"I caught snatches of talk about it, not enough to piece them together into a whole story, but enough to judge that the saint met with abuse at the shrine itself. Chiefly, I was listening to the shepherd." Miguel's face clouded over for a moment. "What happened at the shrine? Is it true that he was humiliated and bruised?"

"Yes," answered Goyo, and smiled at the shepherd. "You're like the saint, Miguel, more anxious to hear than to speak. This is the way it was: the saint reached the monastery church just as the bell for Compline had rung. He made an act of adoration before the Holy Sacrament, then moved quietly to the shrine of the Holy Guadalupe, even though the statue was not to be seen."

"Not to be seen?" Miguel queried. "I thought it was always in view."

"No. Every evening, shortly before the monks chant the

last canonical hour of the Divine Office, the sacristan pulls
a massive velvet drapery over her altar for the night. But
that didn't discourage the saint. Fervently, he made his
devotions before the hidden image and was still in prayer
long after Compline was over and the church had emptied
of monks and pilgrims. Quite alone, he suddenly began to
intone the *Salve Regina.* At the words: *Turn, then, most
gracious Advocate, thine eyes of mercy toward us,* the hanging drew aside of itself, and, as it slid across the bar, the
silver rings from which it is suspended clinked and clashed
together with a sound as of metal striking glass. The sacristan was trimming vigil lamps. He heard the jangling of
the rings and rushed to the shrine. Motionless as the image
itself, the saint's eyes were fixed in wonder upon the
serenely sweet face of the little brown Virgin." Goyo
paused, tapped his sandaled foot on the floor.

"Yes?" Miguel inquired with impatience.

"Understandably," continued Goyo, "the sacristan believed the kneeling man had had the audacity to push aside
the hanging. Moreover, he looked poor beyond anything.
His appearance gave the sacristan the idea that he was a
beggar who planned to better his lot by stealing the precious image."

"That man—steal?" Miguel could only gape. "He
wouldn't take a blade of grass from a sheep." For a moment he visualized John's hauntingly grave face; the eyes
magnificently black, honest and deep. "For the sacristan
to have assumed such a thing," he said hotly, "is an out-
rage. I hope he was punished."

Goyo smothered a smile. "Easy, now, Miguel. Don't get
excited. Shall I go on with it?"

"Yes, yes, please."

"Vaya. The next thing, the sacristan's screams were

piercing the hush in the church. 'Thief!' he shrieked. 'Impious thief! Hypocrite! What do you think you are up to? Get out, get out! Brazen beggar!' The saint kept still. He didn't move, except to lower his head. The sacristan was in a rage. 'I'll teach you not to touch Our Lady's altar hanging! I'll teach you!' he roared and savagely kicked the saint. But it was he, not the saint, who crumpled to the floor.''

"Then he was punished," said Miguel, with obvious satisfaction.

"Yes, the leg with which he struck out at the saint was instantly paralyzed. Vaguely at first, then with terrible clarity, he realized there was no strength or feeling in his right leg. Some moments passed before he dared a glance at the image, or at the saint, who had not stirred. Soon he was crying out again, but this time the cries came from a man who saw the wrong he had done. Wailingly he begged the saint's pardon and implored him to obtain his cure through the intercession of the Blessed Guadalupe. As remote as if he'd been a thousand miles away, the saint made no answer to this for so long that the sacristan became terrified. Clutching the saint's arm, he pleaded, 'Pray for me, pray for me, for my soul as well as my leg is in peril. Help me!' "

"How long did that go on?" asked Miguel.

"The sacristan didn't say precisely. A matter of minutes, I suppose. For him, they must have seemed an eternity. Finally, the saint looked at him and said, 'Let us say the *Salve* together.' "

"Why together?" Miguel wanted to know.

"Well, it is the sacristan's opinion that the saint would not offer the prayer alone because then, if a cure were given, none could point to him as being the one who obtained it."

"And it goes without saying," guessed Miguel, "that the use of his leg was restored to the fellow."

"It was, even before the *Salve* was ended. The saint gave the sacristan no chance to breathe a word of gratitude to him, but said, with a hint of reproach in his voice, 'Give thanks to the Queen of Angels, brother, and try to keep your patience in future.' With that, he got to his feet and was gone before the sacristan could shake off the daze he was in."

There was a lull.

Emotion shone in Miguel's eyes. After a moment, his thoughts withdrew from Guadalupe and centered on a shepherd in Fonte-Ovejuna. "You may recall that a while back I mentioned having listened to a shepherd at Don Tomás' house. Do you?"

The two had to search their memories for a second, then they nodded.

"His name is Rosario and he comes from Oropesa. Does Oropesa mean anything to you?"

"Not to me," Goyo said.

"Nor to me. It is a rural district near the border of Spain and Portugal, and it isn't far from Guadalupe. Beyond that—" Ruben shrugged—"I know next to nothing about it. I have never thought of it as a place of any great importance."

"You can change your estimate of it now, my friend. Oropesa is the saint's village, or was. He lived there many years. He, too, was a shepherd," Miguel said proudly, and smiled to himself as if at some secret shared between them. Whatever the secret, it lifted him into a little meditation on the wonderful ways in which shepherds, certain ones, through the ages, have enjoyed the particular favor of God.

"What about Rosario?" prodded Ruben.

"Ah, yes." Miguel jarred himself out of his dreaming. "He saw the saint in Oropesa. Apparently, he left Guadalupe at about the same time as yourselves and returned to Oropesa for a visit. A specter in rags, nobody recognized him, at least not at first."

"Rags?" Ruben's eyebrows went up in surprise. "That's odd," he said.

Goyo agreed. "Very odd. The Prior gave him a straight, sober tunic of warm white wool. The last time we saw him, he was wearing it."

"Obviously, he gave it to some beggar in exchange for rags," reasoned Miguel. "Rosario said that with every gust of wind he expected to see the garment fall to pieces. Those who'd known him and those who hadn't gathered in the plaza to stare at him as at a freak. Even so, for one and all he had an affectionate greeting. But they—" Miguel sighed.

"They had none for him." Ruben finished the sentence for him.

"Worse, Ruben. Former friends avoided him. Others rudely reminded him of the rich, respected man he could have been had he stayed in Oropesa and married the daughter of the mayoral." Miguel kept his eyes fixed on the flames. "According to Rosario, the saint, when he was a shepherd, had only to link his little finger with the girl's to make her wildly happy. To spare her further pain—and her parents humiliation—he did not visit them. In any case, not many villagers were glad to see him. They considered his appearance an affront, his presence an embarrassment. Rosario tried to offset the unpleasantness the saint met with by offering hospitality in his cottage. I suppose everyone waited to see what he would do."

"I can imagine that what he did surprised them," said Ruben, with a grin.

"Even more than you imagine. The Count of Oropesa had recently provided a hospital for the village. More than anything else, the saint wanted to spend the remainder of his stay caring for the sick. Rosario said that the thought alone made the saint's face brighten, as when the sun comes out unexpectedly on a gray and dismal day. He asked him if nursing had become his profession. His reply was brief. He said, 'Now and again.' Then Rosario, who was disturbed by the saint's poverty and look of frailness, put another question, 'As friend to friend, tell me truthfully, what have you been doing?' To that he answered, 'Trying to learn the will of God.' "

Reflectively, Ruben scratched his chin. "Did he serve the sick?"

"Yes, devotedly."

"That's admirable," Ruben said, "but something puzzles me. Why does that necessarily give uncommon importance to the town of Oropesa?"

Miguel warmed to the chance to explain. "One night, while attending a sick man in the hospital, he caught scraps of talk about a woman with an ulcerous leg. She was poor, no longer young, she lived in a crumbling house on an alley in the darkest, dirtiest section of the village. As soon as he could get away for a few minutes, he sought the woman and found her. His only thought was to speak a few comforting words to her. He told her to have patience and to meditate the examples of those who became saints by happily accepting physical suffering for love of God. He sat beside her for a while; then he knelt and prayed for her. She was groaning with anguish. He ceased his praying and looked at the ulcerous leg, unconscious of the scattering of neighbors who had come in and were standing against the walls, watching. Suddenly—" For a moment Miguel faltered, swallowed visibly. "Suddenly," he repeated, "the saint bent his face to the running sore and drew the corruption into his own mouth."

Ruben and Goyo shuddered.

"I know." Miguel gave them an understanding smile. "We are not the only ones. The witnesses to this marvel of self-control and charity sickened and grimaced in horror. One squeamish woman was about to hurry away, but the saint pulled her back. Then, looking from one to the other, he said sternly, 'The Son of God has overcome every disgust to cure our defilements, and we would draw back from the sores of our brethren! Believe me, we may not ignore one opportunity, however painful it may be, to practice charity.' "

"That must have given them pause," remarked Ruben, a little weakly. And Goyo said, "They must also have seen him in a quite different light."

"They didn't see him at all. They saw only the leg. It was clean, perfectly healed. The loathesome ulcer had disappeared. This one and that one examined the leg. Then a wild cry went up: 'Miracle! Miracle! He is a saint!' In the excitement, nobody saw him leave. He left the house, he left Oropesa."

"He didn't return to the hospital?"

"No."

"But why not?"

"Because," said Miguel, "he has an affliction of his own: humility."

There was silence.

Goyo broke it, asking, "Where is he now?"

Miguel replied, "He alone knows that."

# SIXTEEN

ANY little house anywhere in Granada will do.

The memory of this remark made to Father John of Avila flashed through John's mind.

Here it was, right in front of him. He could not believe it. He stared, shut his eyes, then opened them and stared again. "It can't be!" he murmured and moved a step or two closer to examine a signboard that hung across a grilled door. The legend on the board said: *House to Let for the Lodging of the Poor.* The words seemed to take voice and speak to John. How he wanted it! A house for this purpose had been his ceaseless prayer since the moment the Blessed Mother had placed the Holy Infant in his arms and indicated that he was to dress Him. John rightly understood this to mean that henceforth he was to care for Christ's poor.

At a touch, the grille swung open, as though he were expected. Amazed to find it unlocked, John assumed that the occupants had not moved out yet. Hesitantly he entered the vestibule, crossed through to the patio, glanced around, listened. No sound came from the square, run-down and empty house. John considerately looked here, looked there, wishing not to take someone unawares. Convinced, finally, that the house was unoccupied, his slow step grew quick and firm. He walked along the arched passageway that surrounded the patio, went into the rooms off the outside corridor, climbed the creaking stairs to the second floor. Mentally, he rearranged one thing and another, repaired and altered. Fallen plaster, broken tiles, dirt, splintered stairs, these details and others were easily remedied. Having inspected every corner of the house, he carefully closed the door behind him, glanced again at the owner's name and street, which were painted in small letters underneath the big letters on the sign, and went with all haste to find him.

Don Eduardo was not at home. The servant was reluctant to say when he was expected.

John gazed at the servant pleadingly. "May I wait? It is urgent that I see him."

She hesitated, eyeing John's clean but poor attire with suspicion.

"I'll give you no trouble," he said, "and I will gladly wait as long as necessary."

At last, she unlocked the ornamental iron gate, admitted him and, without saying a word, motioned toward a bench near a small fountain in the center of the patio.

Thin jets of liquid crystal leapt into the air, dripped downward with a tinkle and a splash into the fountain basin. Mirrored in the pool were the mingled brilliance of red-orange pomegranate blossoms, yellow jasmine and roses that twined about the carved cedar columns that supported the second-floor gallery of the house. Now and then, as if to rouse him, a soft wind tossed water over John's bare feet. He took no heed of it. Nor was he conscious of the rose petals the wind kept dropping into his lap. He scarcely noticed the fountain or the flower reflections in it. Elbow propped on his knee, chin cupped meditatively in his hand, he saw only the house that was to let for the lodging of the poor.

The longer he waited, the harder he thought, and the errand which he had undertaken on a wave of joy seemed all at once overbold and reckless. Despite his faith in God's help and his trust in the Blessed Virgin's intercession, he could not escape the fact of his poverty. Since his return to Granada, he had seemed less than ever able to assist the poor. He never had sufficient food or clothing to give to even a few, let alone swarms of sick and poor.

Every morning, he attended the earliest Mass. After Mass, he strode to the forests in the foothills of the Sierra Nevada mountains, gathered faggots, then kept the bundles of sticks until evening, when he sold them in the Vivarambla. During the day, he worked at anything that came to hand and that paid him a few coins. Usually, he asked for work in the kitchens of the rich, for then he could save his own meal and salvage scraps from the table. These, together with his day's wages, he later distributed among Granada's poorest and sickest unfortunates. When work was not to be had, he begged alms for the poor.

Soon after nightfall, carrying a basket on his arm, John wandered through the meanest alleys, made the rounds of the cold, damp shelters under the arches of the bridges, walked the colonnades of public buildings. In these places the homeless, the sick, the hungry lay in misery. Not a few died in the streets. Masking his anguish under a benign and cheerful smile, he swept from one to another, divided the contents of his basket with what generosity he could afford, being always painfully aware that none got enough and far too many got nothing.

John of God was but one pauper trying to aid a legion of fellow paupers; the only man in Granada, it seemed, who cared whether they lived or died. Nightly, the city's destitute awaited the quiet approach of the man they fondly called the Father of the Poor. If his basket was empty, no matter; his heart was full. Love for all men was his great gift. His presence alone was a solace and satisfied a yearning for attention in those who otherwise were overlooked. Listless eyes would brighten as they gazed at John's, darkly sparkling. The glow of his sympathy brought warmth and light to the chill gloom that surrounded the poor. Always serenely cheerful, none guessed the pain that was his for the needy and neglected; none knew that night after night, however late the hour, John slipped into some church, prostrated himself before the Blessed Sacrament and cried out imploringly, "Oh, my Savior! Give me the means to help these people! Give me the means!"

Friend of the poor, the poor dogged his steps. One day the extreme hunger of a cluster of beggars took them to the residence of Don Miguel Avis Vanega, for it was there that John, in return for a room in the rich man's house, relieved the cook of menial kitchen chores. When John saw his sick and starving friends come crowding around the hidalgo's kitchen door, his heart turned over in him. In situations like this, he was more apt to feel than to think. His only thought now was to feed his poor. But how? With what? It was too early for leftovers. The main meal was prepared but hadn't yet been served. He looked about him. The cook was not there. He looked at the pinched, wan faces, staring at him, pleading with him not to be angry with them; his mind rang with their words: "Bread, John. Give us bread. For love of God, give us bread. Feed us, Father of the Poor." Shaken by their suffering, unable to turn a deaf ear to their cries for food, John rashly gave to the beggars the meal which was intended for Don Miguel, his family and household.

Presently the cook returned, saw nothing but empty pans, platters and bowls. Mystified, he turned inquiringly to John, to whom one powerfully clear thought had come. He voiced it. "I am guilty, Berto. I gave away what was not mine to give."

"You?" gasped the cook. "You gave away—everything? To whom?"

"Friends. Very poor people, Berto. It was wrong of me, I know. But they were terribly hungry. You don't know what hunger is."

At this, Berto's amazement became rage against John. "You didn't give," he shouted, "you stole!" The next moment, he was calling loudly for Don Miguel. "Señor, señor," he was saying excitedly, "you should never have brought him here, never. He has robbed you, robbed us all of food. He didn't leave you so much as a crumb of bread. All gone, the entire meal. Who got it? Beggars," he said with contempt. "It would serve him right if you sent him away."

"It would indeed, señor," said John.

"Is this true?"

"Yes, señor." John paused, then offered his apologies. After that, he stood mute under the hidalgo's tongue-lashing. His own devouring hunger for humiliations found satisfaction in Don Miguel's justified anger.

"Thief! Get out, get out!"

John had heard those words before. Quietly he left. No sooner was he out of the house than other servants went in. No one knew them, no one had ever seen them before, nor could it be learned from where they came. But each came laden with delicacies and wines that would have been rare at a king's feast.

Don Miguel, his family and servants followed the train

of silent trencher bearers into the proudly handsome dining room and looked on stupefied at the great variety of viands. Puff pastries filled with spiced pork and lamb; piping hot vegetables dipped in batter and fried to a golden crispness. There were partridge pies, squab, seafood, salads of emerald green lettuce leaves pricked with pomegranate seeds as with jewels; cakes crunchy with ground hazelnuts and almonds; ices colored and flavored with fruits that no one could identify; rich custards topped with cream or drenched in liquid caramel; fritter balls stacked in pyramids that glistened with honey of a fragrance that suggested the roselike scent of raspberries.

The hidalgo raised questioning eyes to each of the numerous servants. Exceptionally swift, hush-footed and stately, all wore a strange little smile. None, however, spoke a word or answered a question. Then, as suddenly as they had come, the mysterious bringers of this most mysterious dinner vanished from view. Miguel Avis Vanega could but assume that he was face to face with a miracle. He more than forgave John. He offered extravagant apologies and begged John to return to his household, to no avail.

Forgiven or not, the lesson John learned then was one he could not forget. It was the memory of the dinner he gave to the poor that made him uneasy now. He had done one man out of his meal. Was he to do another out of his rent? True, the house with the sign on the door was in bad shape. Nevertheless, Granada rentals were steep, even for hovels. The house would cost each month twenty times more than he could beg in alms in a year. Where was the confidence he felt when he discussed the subject of a hospital with Father John of Avila? To himself he said aloud: "God is my only help. I must rely on His goodness; then I can put this worrisome matter of rent out of my mind." But he no sooner tried than the dinner he had lavished upon the beggars pushed itself back in. "How can I take that house when I haven't a cent?" A moment later, he was saying: "How can I possibly let it go? The words on the sign were the clearest invitation. Or," he wondered, "were they temptation?"

Slowly he straightened from his stooped position and looked up at a translucent cloud in a sky as blue as hyacinth, blue as the shadowed snows that crowned the Sierra Nevadas. "Most Holy Virgin," he whispered, "be my advocate. Plead my cause with Don Eduardo. I will be saving and careful." He smiled hopefully, as if the Queen of Heaven were in the cloud. "Please, please, please," he begged. "You know how much I need that house. I will do all the work myself, I promise you."

A stream of wind scattered the cloud. John withdrew his gaze and fixed it on his beads. To the trickle of fountain water and the swish of ramblers swaying in the breeze, he murmured Hail Marys. With each swing of the climbing roses, with the telling of each bead, a red rain of rose petals floated over him, held by the rough cloth of the beggar's shift in which he was dressed.

He did not hear the iron grille open and clang shut, he did not know that Don Eduardo was there. At sight of the tall man on the stone bench, Don Eduardo's heart jumped. The seller of faggots! The saint! Many an evening had he seen him in the Vivarambla, his bundles of firewood strewn about him, and always the string of black beads slipping through those tapering fingers. But Don Eduardo's mind was busy with something more wonderful than that recollection.

On his way home, he had stopped to make a visit at the

church of Our Lady of Victory. To his surprise, he saw
a large crowd of men and women kneeling before the main
altar, staring as if hypnotized at the great crucifix above
it. He, too, looked at it, saw nothing unusual. When one
of the men got up to leave the church, Don Eduardo,
frankly curious, followed him out. Before he could open
his mouth, the man said, "Granada has a saint."

"Yes? Who is he?"

"The wood vendor. Regularly at sundown he goes to
the Vivarambla to sell faggots. You may have seen him.
Almost everyone has."

"I have."

"For a while," said the man who introduced himself
as Pedro Solano, "the vendor worked in the kitchen of
Miguel Avis Vanega and—" He was cut short by the other
who declared, "The whole city knows about that. Tell
me, señor, why were you and the others looking so steadily
at the crucifix?"

Eagerly Pedro Solano replied, "Perhaps two hours ago
it happened. About a dozen of us were in the church. The
wood vendor was on his knees before the *Santisimo Cristo,*"
he said, referring to the crucifix. "Then she came."

"She?"

"Our Lady, señor. It can have been no other. Someone
was with her. Some witnesses said the Blessed Virgin was
accompanied by Saint John the Evangelist. I cannot vouch
for it. An apparition, yes; I am sure there was one, although
I saw nothing except the saint's face. It was upraised, vivid
as light itself. His hands were crossed on his breast. He
did not stir at all; there was only this radiance. Everyone
saw it and saw it become brighter and brighter as, seemingly, the vision moved toward him."

Pedro Solano paused. Perspiration broke out over his

forehead. He flicked it off with the back of his hand, continued gravely, "I, señor, and everyone else in the church, heard distinctly the voice that spoke to him, the voice of the Blessed Virgin, sweet and calm. She said:

*It is by thorns, labors and sufferings you must earn the crown my Son has prepared for you.*

Another pause. "At that very moment, señor, a tremor went through the saint. He shuddered as if with a stabbing pain. Then he stiffened, opened his eyes and fastened his gaze upon the crucifix. Our eyes followed his. It was then that a woman screamed, 'Look! Look! The crown of thorns!' " Pedro glanced at Don Eduardo. "No doubt you are familiar with the crucifix high above the altar?"

Yes, he had seen it innumerable times.

"Then you know it is woven of real and very long thorns." Pedro was silent for so long that Don Eduardo expected nothing more. Finally he said, "Señor, the crown was missing from the head of Our Lord on the crucifix. Beyond any doubt, Our Lady herself pressed that crown of thorns upon the head of the wood vendor. When he realized what had happened, he flung himself flat on the floor, face down, saying over and over:

*My adorable Savior . . . Your thorns will be roses for me. . . .*

Peering into the church, Don Eduardo looked once again at the crucifix which soon was to become known as the Crucifix of the Apparition of the Crowning with Thorns. "It is there now," he remarked, marveling.

Pedro Solano nodded. "He, too, would be there now, still in ecstasy, but for the cries of 'stigmata!' 'miracle!' and 'saint!' The words rippled and echoed through the church. Somebody went running for the priest. The excitement shocked the saint out of the rapture he was in. He was up in a flash, like that. Gone," Pedro Solano said, "gone with the swiftness of a shadow."

Now as he stood behind a veil of yellow jasmine that trailed downward from the upper gallery, it all seemed more like a dream than reality to Don Eduardo. Barefoot, bareheaded, wearing a dull gray tunic, it was difficult, looking at this man, to imagine the Most Holy Virgin descending from above to mark him with the divine stigmata of Jesus Christ. Yet she it was, Mary, full of grace, who had pressed the thorns into his flesh. At the same time, Don Eduardo sensed something in the pure, clear-cut profile, in the steadfast way in which he kept his eyes upon his rosary crucifix, that made him crave his blessing. To ask it, however, would be to show a reverence that the saint would not tolerate, for his humility was as much a marvel as the miracles and apparitions with which God favored him. Now, too, it suddenly occurred to Don Eduardo to wonder why the saint was here. His first glimpse of John had given him such a start that he hadn't stopped to think of anything except Pedro Solano's account of the apparition. To himself he said, I must pretend I just came home. I must pretend I am ignorant of what happened at Our Lady of Victory.

His nervousness hidden under the formal courtesy of the Spanish gentleman, Don Eduardo greeted John, who got up at the sound of the quick, direct footsteps and looked down from his height with that friendly intentness and the warm smile that made most strangers his friends at the first encounter.

How curious to find a saint so easy to meet! Don Eduardo's anxiety vanished instantly. It was John who felt the palms of his hands beginning to perspire and who could not bring himself to speak.

"Was there something you wanted to see me about?" Don Eduardo opened the conversation quietly.

"Yes, señor." John inclined his head, as though he were afraid of saying what his errand was. After a moment, he looked up, went on. "I came about the house that is to let for the lodging of the poor." His voice was a little tight with worry.

"The house is yours," said Don Eduardo with a genial finality that startled John. "Sit down, please," he urged, and sat beside his guest on the bench. "You look distressed. Why?"

"I've reason enough." John planted his long hands on his knees and stared at the water in the pool. "You are kinder than you are prudent, señor."

"I don't understand. You said you came about the house. If you want it, it is yours."

"I want it very much. But you don't know me, or anything about me."

Lightly, Don Eduardo said, "I know that you sell faggots in the Vivarambla. I have seen you there. I also know that many beggars follow you about and speak of you as the Father of the Poor."

"Are you aware, señor, that I am one of them?"

"Well, yes, more or less."

"In all fairness," said John honestly, "I must tell you that I have no money. By some I am thought to be a madman. There are others who would be justified in calling me a thief."

Don Eduardo gave no sign that he had heard. "You want the house," he said. "Take it."

"I haven't told you for what purpose I want it. The sick poor," John said quietly. "There are so many in Granada. They need help."

"Are you a physician?"

"I? No, señor, I am not a doctor. I am nothing. But God has given me uncommon bodily strength. I should like to use it in the service of His poor. Our Lord helps those who trust in Him. I trust Him to send doctors to my outcasts. Therefore," John reasoned, "they are bound to come."

Don Eduardo thought: You say you are nothing. Yet you are one of God's chosen, and that rarest of men, your brother's keeper. "In short," he said casually, "you wish to convert the house into a hospital."

John beamed. "That is my longing," he said with passion. "If, of course, you have no objection."

"None, none at all, except the state it is in."

"That's nothing. I am handier than I look. Poverty has advantages. It makes one resourceful. Necessity has forced me to discover the way to use tools and clay and white-wash. Give me a week," he said, "and you won't recognize your house." Now the changes that he planned dominated his conversation. Ordinarily, what went on in the depths of his mind was not put in words. But when he was exuberant about something, he spoke with contagious excitement. Imaginative and original, as well as practical, John's ideas were newly thought, inspired by the situation at hand. With verve and enthusiasm, he explained and described his plans, and it was soon more than evident that where the care of the sick was concerned, he was anything but ignorant. He was well informed.

John's first benefactor listened attentively to every word, grateful to be able to contribute to the saint the house that was to be his first hospital, the first of its kind. Monastic Orders, semi-religious and semi-military Orders, and sovereigns founded, staffed and supported hospitals through-

out Europe, and had for centuries. But as far as Don
Eduardo or anyone else knew, this was the first instance
of a solitary individual who was neither monk, knight
nor prince, merely a layman who hadn't a roof over his
head or a cent to his name, founding and supporting a
hospital completely on his own.

By turns Don Eduardo listened to his guest in astonishment, and by turns he found himself discreetly staring
at John's head for proof of the stigmata. As was the case
with many other Saints on whom the marks of nails, spear
and thorns were supernaturally impressed, and remained
unseen, so too it was with John of God. The hand of Saint
Catherine of Siena, lacerated by a nail that Christ drove
through it, appeared perfectly smooth, yet the pain in her
hand was ever present. The pain in John's head was to
be always with him too, every thorn stab burning like a
point of fire. The heavenly wounds, however, were invisible. They were to become visible rather in his spirit,
for day after day he was to relive the Sacred Passion in his
soul.

Visualizing the dream that was about to materialize,
John said, "As soon as I am able, I will pay for the use
of the house."

"What? Oh, that. Forget it. I don't want payment for it.
I repeat, the house is yours. Do with it what you please."

His face transfigured by an expression of gratitude and
love, John laid his hand on Don Eduardo's shoulder, while
his glance went skyward. "Wonderful, wonderful," he
murmured. "I saw no way to have the house, no way. I
begged Our Lady to press my cause with you. See what
she has done for me! Brother, go to Our Lady whether
you have needs or not. Recite her rosary as often as you
can. You will find it rewarding. She listens even to callous

sinners like myself. To catch her attention is already a greater kindness than I deserve; to have her obtain from her Son the one thing that I wanted desperately is—" John stopped, gestured helplessly. Elated, he finally declared, "There is no word for what it is."

After a moment, Don Eduardo asked, "Who will assist you?"

"Assist me?" The compelling black eyes looked away from the sky to the benefactor. "At what, señor?"

"At everything."

John laughed gently. "Nobody," he replied.

Forgetting that the zeal of a saint is sufficiently powerful to enable him to accomplish superhuman tasks, Don Eduardo saw John killing himself before ever he got around to caring for the sick poor. "You can't do it alone," he insisted. "I wonder, did you have a look at the house?"

"I had a good look."

"Then how—?" Don Eduardo broke off, thought a moment. "Look," he said, "the least I can do is to send a carpenter to help with the repairs. Let me do that much, will you?"

John did not reply at once. Quite suddenly, he noticed the rose petals that clung to the scratchy cloth of his shift. Silently, he said: *Your thorns will be roses for me.* And silently he recalled a promise made to the Blessed Virgin Mary. He gave a smile of extraordinary sweetness to the man at his side and shook his head.

"But why not?" Don Eduardo asked.

With a touch of the secretive, John said: "Because I may not. It is the first step and I must take it alone."

# SEVENTEEN

**H**OW old are you, John?"

The hands that busily scoured supper dishes in a great basin of hot, soapy water were still for a second. "How old?" John shot the questioner a quizzical glance. "Going on forty-five," he said. "Why, Doctor? You aren't thinking that I ought to quit, are you?" John smiled. "Christopher Columbus," he said, "was forty-six before he discovered America. Would you have said to him, 'Forget your charts and maps, old sailor. Just take it easy while you wait to die.'?"

"Who said anything about quitting? For you, I cannot imagine a more futile suggestion."

"Something's on your mind," said John and went back to his dishwashing.

Something was. Doctor Sandoz scrutinized him anxiously. How long could he last at the pace at which he was going? Hardly had he opened his first hospital before he was forced to look for larger quarters. The search led to his present and second hospital, an abandoned Carmelite monastery. Don Eduardo's house had proved far too small, accommodating only forty-six beds, which meant forty-six patients, for John firmly insisted upon an innovation that was practically unheard of in sixteenth-century hospitals: every patient must have his own bed. Not for anything would he permit two sick persons to share a bed. The alms

of a royal chaplain provided the first forty-six beds, as well
as mattresses, linens, blankets and bolsters. Now, as then,
John made all the necessary repairs, bought furniture,
linens, utensils, dishes, carried it all to his hospital, fash-
ioned wooden crosses which he placed at the head of each
bed, in order to constantly remind himself of Christ Crucified in the persons of his patients. When all was in readi-
ness, he combed the alleys and river banks, looking for the
sick who were most in need of attention. Having found
them, he carried them in his arms, or over his shoulders,
to the refuge he had prepared.

Charitable doctors came, as John knew they would come.
Meticulously, he executed their orders and filled their
prescriptions with a skill and knowledge that amazed them.
Priests made daily visits to his hospital and often remained
with his patients when it was necessary for John to go out
on some errand. The first step had indeed been taken, and
quite alone, except for the services of doctors and priests.

If it bewildered the imagination to think of one man
nursing forty-six people, cooking, cleaning, laundering,
bathing and feeding the sick, praying with them morning
and evening, hearing Mass every morning, journeying from
end to end of Granada each night to collect food, clothing,
bed linens and alms for the needs of his poor, it was more
staggering yet to realize that now he was in attendance
upon a hundred and twenty-five patients. His enormous
compassion drove him to do more yet. In the afternoons,
when he usually could find a priest to stay with his patients,
John slipped out to find the hovels of the poor whose pride
stood in the way of their coming to him for help. He no
sooner heard about these cases than he appeared. Sweet-
natured, passionately devoted to the needy and the sick,
his manner instantly turned embarrassment into gratitude

and relief. The first social worker of his day, John of God cleaned the houses of the poor, took food with him and cooked it, bathed and dressed the children, the aged, the helpless. Everything in sight was washed and scrubbed with boiling water. This simple means of sterilizing clothes, bedding, towels, pots and pans, dishes, furniture, walls and floors was another of his innovations. His own worries and fatigue seemed to him trifling as against the misery that he saw. In his selfless desire to do something for homeless and hungry men, he made a night shelter of the monastery vestibule, the patio and the cloister walks that surrounded it. Hordes came to him for overnight refuge, and to these hordes he served supper and gave clean pallets of woven fiber, pillows and blankets.

Watching him with as great perplexity as worry, Doctor Sandoz said, "You accomplish more in one day than twenty men could do in a week. Take care, or you'll work yourself into the narrow width of your grave long before your time."

"Before my time or not," John was saying, as he lifted soapy bowls and rinsed them in scalding water, "as long as I can accomplish God's work, that's all that matters."

"Seriously, John, you ought to let up a little."

"Let up? You mean—rest?" The thought was foreign to him. "Doctor, I have only begun, and I am not doing half enough."

"You're not doing what you tell others to do, that's certain."

"No?"

"No," echoed the Doctor. "To everyone you say, 'Three things we must do every day: pray, work and sustain the body.' You pray and you work, but you don't sustain your body."

"Don't worry about me, Doctor. With God's help, I can do whatever He wants me to do. If nothing else," he smiled, "these dishes are going to be clean, clean, clean." Once again, there was a torrent of boiling water pouring over hundreds of mugs, bowls and plates. John exulted in it.

"And if you indulge yourself in nothing else," remarked the Doctor, "you use water with glorious abandon."

"Water is meant to be used. Ah, Doctor, the times I've wished I could have the Moors' old *Albaicin* for a hospital! Only the Moors would equip a fortress with baths. I went there once to see them. Sunken baths of smooth marble. The vaulted roofs over the cubicles are fretted with star-shaped openings. My next hospital shall have sunken baths," he said lightheartedly. "Until then, ewers and basins."

"The way you've squandered water on those dishes, it would surprise me if you have a drop left to put into a ewer."

"Hardly more than a drop," John said, staring down into a huge copper kettle. "First thing in the morning, I'll have to go to the Vivarambla fountain."

"Send Ramon," said the Doctor.

"I can't. He's convalescing. I let him help me serve the meals, but he isn't strong enough for heavier work than that. Besides, it needs a man my size to carry the water jars."

Doctor Sandoz' eyes followed the direction of John's forefinger to a corner of the arched and low-ceilinged kitchen. He gasped. "Those huge things are water jars? They're big enough to bathe in. Where on earth did you get them?"

"From Abdul, a Moorish potter. He gave them to me in

exchange for catechism lessons. They are supposed to be used for storing olive oil. Without jars as big as those, I'd be most of the day going to and from the fountain."

"Even empty, I couldn't lift one, let alone filled," declared the Doctor. "How do you manage it?"

"I rope two or three to my back at a time. It's simple," John said, with as little concern as if they were small ornamental vases.

"Two or three!" Dumfounded, Doctor Sandoz dropped to a bench and, as though he were overheated from having lugged the immense jars up Granada's hilly streets, he flung open his long scarlet robe, the mark of the sixteenth-century physician. "What an incredible man you are! Incredible. I'd give you a donkey for the purpose, except I know what would happen."

"I know, too. The donkey would balk. I'd worry about baths, beds and meals, and, in the end, I'd have the donkey in my arms and the jars on my back. Thank you, Doctor, but don't bother." John smiled, laid out clean towels and proceeded to dry the mountain of dishes.

While John dried and hummed, the Doctor sat very still, thinking. John had a way of making people think. Not only had he kept his word that he would do all the work, he had also kept his word that he would be saving and careful. Rather than buy faggots, each day he gathered his own. He needed great bundles of them for his cooking fires and for the fires that perpetually crackled under kettles in which water was perpetually boiling. If time ran out on him and he couldn't go to the forests, he went to the river Genil and fished out armfuls of sticks that drifted on the current. Frugal in the extreme with himself, he saved everything for his poor, within his hospital and out.

To John of God, nursing the sick was more than a profession. It was the embodiment of sympathy and boundless love. It was self-dedication to the suffering for the
glory of God, and for the glory of God he saw to it that
the patient's first thought was his soul's salvation. In imitation of Christ Who washed the feet of His Apostles, John,
on admitting or bringing to his hospital a sick man he'd
found in the streets, washed the patient's feet, kissed them
and then presented the crucifix to be kissed. Tenderly, he
removed the sick man's rags. If they were beyond mend-
ing, he burned them; if not, he boiled them and put them
to some use. Then he bathed the patient, dressed him in a
clean gown and carried him to a clean bed. Immediately
he would say, "Thank God, brother, that He gives you
time to do penance. I will fetch the priest. He will heal
your soul. As to your body, do not trouble. It will be looked
after with care."

At break of day, John heard Mass. Then he went singing
through the wards, "Come along, brothers, let us give
thanks to God." He led them in prayer, then read to them
either from *The Imitation of Christ,* the Epistles or the
Gospels. After morning prayer, he bathed every patient,
changed the linens on every bed and, whether he spoke
or not, gave heart to all. His tall, cheerful, immaculate
presence seemed to send out currents of strength to the
weak and courage to the frightened. In his judgment, the
sick more than others needed sympathy and love. He gave
of both unstintingly and wrought more good by his personal magnetism and the influence of his piety than all
the pills and potions in the world.

These chores completed, he flew to the kitchen, prepared
breakfast for more than a hundred sick, served it, gathered
up the trays, returned to the kitchen to wash the dishes.

Then came the daily washing of gowns and linens, and the thorough scrubbing of floors. With scarcely a second to call his own, he prayed and meditated at his work, which to him was not tiresome drudgery but an unmerited privilege, for in serving the poor he served his Savior.

Now, too, his former career as a soldier stood him in good stead. He regulated the routine of his hospital with a kind of military discipline and punctuality. Every minute was accounted for. Without strict adherence to a carefully planned schedule, he would have foundered. Misspent moments would have been as so many leaks in a sinking ship. There was a time for this and a time for that. At a given hour in the morning, and again in the evening, John visited with every patient in his wards. By reserving certain wards for certain types of illnesses, he set another precedent, brought about another change in established custom. He isolated contagious from noncontagious diseases; mild and temporary disorders from incurable and chronic ones. He had separate wards for surgical cases, cripples and the insane.

To those afflicted with mental diseases, John of God gave especial care, thought and love. If he rocked the physicians by his theories, they nevertheless submitted to him. It was that or nothing. Boldly he expressed his views and boldly he stood by them. The hospital was his, and treatment of the insane must be administered according to his directions. Astonished by the results, his doctors were convinced that his mind was divinely illuminated. In his ward for the insane, the quiet was almost unbroken. No hysterical screams, no violent sobbing. No lash. No men chosen for their brute strength to stand guard and apply the whip. The atmosphere was bright, tranquil and clean. A few simple drugs were given. But in the main, improvement was due to John of God's sound sense. Instead of floggings, starvation and the intentional prevention of sleep by unmerciful devices, John's patients were treated with Christlike patience and love; they received nourishing food, great amounts of sleep, sunshine and fresh air.

His dependents increased, his power to assist them dwindled—but never his faith. God would listen. The Blessed Mother would listen. They had to. No day passed but he confronted tragedy. Abandoned babies, orphans, widows alone, widows with hungry, ill-clad children; aged men without homes; the paralyzed, the blind. In his heart there was room for all. But he needed houses for them, too; houses that he could supervise. It was in the afternoons, usually, when he pursued his various errands of mercy, that his way seemed filled with thorns and stones and darker than his wanderings by night. Yet, by the time he got home again, his brain was spinning with plans and ideas. His step was as light as if he'd rested for hours, as he hurried to his kitchen to start supper.

Toward nine at night, with the same dedicated duty that kept him moving all day, John of God, who wanted nothing for himself, set forth to beg for his poor. With a basket on his back, a wide kettle hanging from each arm, a bell in his hand, he walked from street to street. His bell announced his coming. At spaced intervals, he silenced the bell, and his voice rose as in a holy chant: "Who wants to do good to himself? Brothers, for love of Our Lord Jesus Christ, do good to yourselves. Give to the poor. Do good to yourselves." His bell and cry opened purses and cupboards. John of God with his basket, kettles and bell became as familiar a sight at night as the candle-lanterns that dimly lit his paths.

Midnight found him on his knees in prayer for his bene-

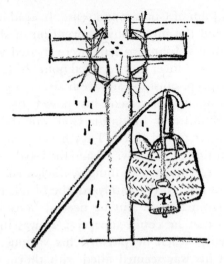

factors. Hours later he was still in prayer. He abided by his own words: "The heart of a Christian should never sleep." His heart never slept. It was constantly awake to the needs of others. He was equally faithful to another of his sayings: "He who vows for God to toil, His work by slumber must not spoil." He still fended off sleep for all but one hour. Having neither cell nor bed, he spent that hour stretched out under the staircase, where he lay on stones with a stone for a pillow. His only covering was a clean but threadbare cloak left by one of his beggars.

Slowly, Doctor Sandoz emerged from his thinking as from a dream. But he had not been dreaming. John of God's endless round of chores was true, a true and continuous miracle. It was no surprise to the Doctor to see the kitchen in perfect order and John vanished. Closing his scarlet gown, he rose, took his staff and made his way out. John's night-shelter was crowded with men. Doctor Sandoz looked from one to the other, quietly measuring the strength of each. Hope faded. He shook his head. There wasn't one among them who looked strong enough to be of any help to John.

His mood was one of grave concern. Somewhere in Granada's tangle of narrow streets walked a barefoot man whose incomparable charity already had worn him down to a shadow. Doctor Sandoz looked about, half-expecting to see him. He went on, his staff sharply striking the stones. Then, just as he crossed under an old archway, he came to a sudden standstill. John's bell! A clear, clean tone, clean as the triumphant rags of the man who rang it. And now his voice: *Brothers, do good to yourselves!* The kindly Doctor wished that somebody would do good to John, fill not only his basket and skillets but his dire need for assistance. Little did he dream how soon his wish was to be granted. Still less did he dream the nature of the help that John was to receive. How could he know? Doctor Sandoz was wishing in terms of mortal men.

# EIGHTEEN

FAR above the rust-red towers of the palace of the ancient Moorish kings, the sun was high in a sky as vividly bright as blue stained glass. The sound of fountain water mingled with the chirping of birds, the rattle of tambourines and the low-voiced talk of vendors who arrived from all directions and turned the middle of the plaza into an open-air market.

Lazily, two young vendors ambled toward the Vivarambla fountain, looked up, came to a sudden stop.

"It can't be!" said Matias, the seller of small water jars.

"Nevertheless it is. There's only one man in Granada," said Tano, "who uses oil jars for water, only one who can lift them as if they were weightless. By my life, he must have iron in his hands. My trayful of *Agnus Dei* medals to one of your yellow clay jars, if he wanted to, he could pull the horns off a bull with the greatest of ease."

Curious, the pair walked around the fountain and stared at John of God, who was frowning, chewing his lip and hurriedly roping the huge containers to his back.

"The Father of the Poor is late this morning," ventured Matias, his brows raised in surprise.

John glanced at him and flushed. "Yes, very late."

"A beggar waylaid you, eh?"

"Not a beggar, an enemy." There was self-reproach in John's voice.

194

"Most good men have enemies," Tano assured him.

"Have they? I wouldn't know, not being a good man."

Matias grinned. "That can be remedied." He paused. Teasingly he said, "Do good to yourself, brother. Alms, for the love of God. One *blanca*," he whined, mimicking the cry of Granada's other beggars for the least valuable of Spanish coins. "Only one little *blanca*. Then I can study for the priesthood and never again feel want or worry."

"That's all you know about it. Don't jest, Matias. I'm not in the mood." John sighed. In spite of his disgust with himself, he smiled at them. "Work is pleasing to God," he said. "Be about yours and leave me to mine." He turned from the fountain and sped away home, the jars on his back like two dripping red cupolas.

Soon he appeared in the largest of his wards. It was shiningly clean and washed in sunlight. In the presence of his poor, who affectionately called him Father or Father John, the saint was as a servant in the midst of lords. Humbly he stood before them. His face colored with shame. He begged, "Forgive me, my children. Your lazy, worthless father is unpardonably late this morning. I have kept you waiting. I have upset the whole routine." Then, as though he had committed a grave sin, he admitted "I overslept." After a moment, he said, "Have patience. The water is warming now. I'll soon have you bathed, and then I'll bring your breakfast. Bear with me and beg God to pardon my neglect of you." He was on his way out when a convalescent called him back.

"Not now, Vicente." Gently, he pleaded with the youth. "What you have to say to me can keep a while. I must get on with my work."

"You've done your work. That's what I'm trying to tell you."

John was bewildered. This had been a morning indeed, with oversleeping, getting behind in all his chores, racing to the fountain and home again, with Matias and now Vicente making ill-timed jests. He tried to speak calmly. "Through my fault, Vicente, everything is in a muddle. The moment I have caught up with myself, I will listen to whatever it is you want to say. Would you see all your brothers starve for their breakfast?"

"Starve! After the way we stuffed ourselves? Starve!" Vicente's dark head fell back on the pillow in a peal of laughter. Then he sat upright again. "Father, you didn't oversleep. We wish you would. You are doing too much; you work so hard that you cannot remember what you have done. You bathed us, changed our gowns and linens, brought us breakfast—and what a breakfast! Later, you came back to scrub and polish the floor." Before John could say anything, Vicente continued, "The rich must have come flocking to the jangling of your bell last night. How did you get all that food into one basket and two kettles? Melons, pomegranates, grapes, oranges!"

"What are you talking about, Vicente?"

"Breakfast. You gave us anything we fancied. And the bread was still warm from the oven. Bread with honey."

For several long moments John stood silent. He watched the sunshine stream in through the windows in a shimmering flow of light that fell on the bed coverlets, each as white and smooth as a drift of snow; it shone on the spotless whitewashed walls, on the gleaming maroon tile floor. Mystified, he regarded Vicente seriously; then he walked over to his bed. "Don't sit up, Vicente. Lie down and stay still."

"Lie down? Why?"

"I don't know the reason, but you're overexcited."

"Nothing of the kind, Father. I'm overfed. Otherwise, I'm fine. I want to get up." Vicente dropped his glance. His restless fingers plucked at the sheet. "Let me help in the kitchen," he petitioned, not looking at John. "Ramon helps you. Not much, but some."

Standing at the foot of the bed, John smiled at the little edge of envy in the words. It gladdened him that his boys wanted to be useful. Vicente and Ramon had lived most of their lives in the streets. Neither knew whether he was orphaned or abandoned, but each knew that he was alone. The one John had found on the banks of the Genil, a knife wound in his shoulder. His first encounter with Vicente had been outside a wine-house. The boy was sprawled on the stones. Someone within the wine-house had all but split his skull by bringing a beaker down on it.

"Don't pluck the sheet to shreds," John said to Vicente, and gave his big toe a tweak. "About letting you help, I'll see what Doctor Sandoz says after he has examined you this afternoon. All right?"

Vicente's face brightened. "He'd better see Ramon, too," he said.

"Why? Does his shoulder bother him?"

"No, you bother him." Humor flickered in Vicente's eyes. "He was here right after you polished the floor. He had the look of a fallen hero. I guess he feels fallen. He was puffing and panting and saying all at once, 'I was too late to bring the trays up, too late to take them down. I couldn't keep apace of our Father this morning. *Ay de mi!* This Father of ours! One, two, three, everything was done! He was here, he was there, flitting from room to room like a blown feather, while I, always a league behind him, I hobbled along like a worn-out pilgrim with pebbles in his sandals. I was no help with the meal trays, so I thought I'd ask if he'd trust me to do the dishes. Same thing. By the time I got to the kitchen, the dishes were done. He was putting away the last plate.' "

Smiling a little, John backed a step away from Vicente's bed. "Now you've had your fun with me. May I go? If I don't hurry, the water for your baths will be boiling over."

The man in the bed next to Vicente's spoke up. "You bathed us fully two hours ago."

"I did not."

"Yes, you did. And Vicente wasn't poking fun at you. What he said is true, every word of it. By the Blessed Angels, Father, who should know that better than you? Vicente is right. You ought to oversleep. You need rest."

John drew a long, quivering breath. "Brothers, brothers," he protested firmly, "I know nothing of this—this fantasy. How could I? Last night I used up all the water. When I awakened this morning and realized how late it was, I didn't take time to hear Mass, even. I went at once to the Vivarambla fountain." John saw every pair of eyes fixed upon him in disbelief. Slowly, and accenting every word, he continued, "I went to the fountain for water. I filled my jars. Must I call in witnesses? I could, at that. I exchanged a few words with two vendors. I only just now came home. For me to have done what you say I did would be humanly impossible. I tell you, I was not here."

"Yes, you were. You attended every patient in every ward. Ramon followed you about, although he scarcely ever caught up with you."

John shook his head, gave a short laugh and said, "Brothers, I have been many things in my time, but not until now a phantom." Truly puzzled, he stood staring at the floor and saw himself clearly mirrored in its glassy luster. He thought: It has an unusual burnish. I didn't give it that. He glanced up abruptly. "Whoever our friend is," he said, "he is a person of marvelous charity. When I find him, I will pour out my thanks."

Laughter rippled over the ward.

Vicente said, "When you find him? You haven't far to look. Thank yourself, Father, for it was you, no other."

The next moment John hurried out, bent on searching the hospital for its benefactor. He came upon no one except his patients. One and all related the same story he had heard in the first ward, and everybody insisted that he himself had seen to their comfort, then put everything in perfect, gleaming order. The human helpmate he expected to find did not materialize. Gravely, he considered every conceivable natural explanation, only to eliminate each by the sheer force of logic. Then something stirred in his mind. Recently, a celestial figure had appeared to him to promise support if he needed it. At the time, John wasn't certain whether the vision was actual or a thing he had dreamed, for there was a vagueness about it all, save for the plainly voiced promise. Even now, he could not have said definitely whether he had looked upon an angel or a saint. Strong was his feeling, however, that God, Who can bestow His mercy through heavenly beings or mortals, whichever one He pleases, had in this instance used an angel.

With a bounding heart, John flashed from ward to ward like a newly fanned flame, his face, his whole body aglow with that special elation which pervaded his being with a brightness that was distinctively his own. To his sick he caroled his song of joy: "Praised be Jesus Christ! My

brothers, let us thank Him for His kindness to us. He must
dearly love His poor when He sends angels to wait upon
them!"

Who was the angel?

The same who was to appear some years hence to a high-
born priest of Cordoba, Don Andres Roelas. And just as
he already had offered his services to John of God, the
angel, at God's command, was to offer to take under the
protection of his shimmering wings the once-Moorish city
of Cordoba. For thirty minutes, it is said, the priest and
the angel discussed this unique proposition, each of them
occupying a handsome chair of Spanish leather bearing
the crest of the nobleman-priest tooled in gold on the back.

John of God's second encounter with the angel occurred
in a quite opposite setting from that in Cordoba, but one
wholly in character with the Father of the Poor, who was
neither nobleman nor priest. It happened soon after the
morning that John overslept. The place was a wretched
street where run-down houses huddled close together and
a few candle-lanterns threw a dim light, late at night, over
images of saints set in niches above the doors. Ever alerted
to the slightest sound of human suffering, John was
brought up short by a man's weak moans. They came from
almost at his feet. Quickly, he knelt beside the prostrate
figure on the chill, sharp stones and laid his hand on a
bony shoulder that felt dry and feverish to the touch. The
haggard face was wet with chill perspiration.

Feeling a hand on his shoulder, the old man opened his
eyes and at once recognized the face above him. Enfeebled
hands clutched at John's tunic. "Take me with you, Father
of the Poor. Take me. Help me."

John nodded. "Yes, brother, yes. That is why I am here."
He saw the drooping lids close again and heard the faint

voice saying, "If only you could take me! But I cannot walk. I will be too much for you, with your full hamper and kettles." Even so, the decrepit man looked at him pleadingly and seized a fold of his tunic with what little grip he had left in his skeletal hands.

John, whose eyes welled for a moment, as when he contemplated the exhausted Christ on the Cross, smiled his benign smile and put his hand on the aged one's cheek. "Never fear, brother, you'll be no burden. I am strong as Sampson, and my power is in my muscles, not in my hair. It will be my happiness to serve you. Come along." Very gently, he lifted the withered man off the ground. "Lock your arms about my neck and rest your head on my shoulder. That's it." In one lithe movement, he was on his feet, walking at his easy stride in the direction of his hospital.

All that John of God could give went out of him to his poor. He gave comfort, care and love. In return, they, without knowing it, gave him a continual experience of the Passion. Regardless of the nature, their torments and misfortunes racked his spirit. Sick bodies and sick souls alike ensnared him in the web of their disorders. And now, to his own astonishment, he felt in his physical person the limpness and debility of the starved man he was carrying. As his vigor began to ebb, he stumbled and swayed. The wasted frame in his arms seemed to have become a man cut in granite. The look on John's face changed from pity to alarm. Silently he prayed, "Lord! Most compassionate Lord! Give me strength. Don't let me fall and injure this poor man." It was John's forehead that was dripping now, John's body that quivered like a tapering cypress shaken by the wind. To no avail, he struggled to steady his trembling limbs. His knees buckled and he fell. Bitterly he rebuked his spent body for being cowardly and worthless.

Quite suddenly, out of the shadows, a handsome youth emerged, glinting and glowing. His legs were sheathed in rose-red trunkhose. He wore breeches, doublet, cloak and cap of silk of a bright, luminous blue. His doublet was belted with gold. Cape and cap were embroidered in thread of gold and spattered with jewels as with drops of moonlight of palest green. A Spanish grandee of great name, thought John, and was amazed at seeing so dazzling a gentleman in such a place. Easily, the stranger gathered up the sick man into his own silken arms. To John he said, "Why do you chide your body, when you overload it?"

Still shaky, John picked himself up off the stones. "My trouble is not with my load," he sighed, "but with a body that is pampered and does not wish to work. Please God, I may conquer it." He gave a tired smile to the stranger. "Brother, how am I to thank you for your charity?"

The radiantly clad hidalgo made no reply to this. But he said, "Link your arm in mine. You're trembling like a harp unstrung."

Together they walked in silence, until John said, "Under that arch, then up the three steps and around the corner to your right."

"I know the way to your hospital, Father of the Poor."

"You do?" John's dark eyes fixed themselves wonderingly on the perfect profile.

"Doesn't everyone know your hospital and your work?"

Averting his gaze from the richly attired youth, John answered quietly, "I can speak only for the poor. They know where to find me and I know where to find them." He hesitated. "You have been most kind to my patient and to me. Please do not think me unduly rude, but may I ask your name?"

"You may. My name is Raphael. I am the angel Raphael, whom God has appointed to assist and protect you and all those who will aid you in your works of charity." * Freighted with meaning, the brief announcement was made without pomp. Rather, the almost matter-of-fact manner of the angel suggested that it was the usual thing

---

* A somewhat similar message was given by the same angel to Don Andres Roelas, May 7, 1578. Inscribed on a monument which commemorates the appearance of the angel to the priest in Cordoba, the legend reads: *Yo te juro por Jesu-Cristo cruzificado que soi Rafael Angel, a quien Dios tiene puesto por guarda de esta ciudad.*—I swear by Jesus Christ crucified that I am the Angel Raphael, whom God has appointed guardian of this city.

for Almighty God to send an archangel to support and associate himself with a mortal.

Overawed and bewildered, John stood like a stone statue of himself. What had happened was beyond human understanding, though not beyond believing, not to a man of faith in the power of God. Gradually, John realized that he was staring into empty space. His co-worker had vanished. The old strength was in his arms again; so, too, was the sick man. Just before the stupefying words were spoken, it had been on the tip of John's tongue to say that he hoped he would see his benefactor now and again. He smiled radiantly to himself, for he knew that, visible or invisible, he could count on Saint Raphael being always somewhere near.

John's reliance on his celestial companion was justified. A few evenings later, his patients and the drove of men in his night-shelter appeared to be uncommonly hungry. Heart ruling reason, John was imprudently generous with the bread. Long before he had served a portion to each— and he had close to two hundred mouths to feed—the supply gave out. What to do? Head down, worriedly trying to work out something to give them in place of bread, he glanced up suddenly to see a man come into the kitchen with bread and more bread. The visitor resembled John enough to be his twin. This fact, no less than the crusty loaves, gave the latter a start. More yet, the man was wearing a beggar's robe exactly like his own. Then in a flash he recognized him.

"You!" John beamed. "Oh, thanks be to God! I can use that bread immediately. What would I do without you, my—my—?" He paused, colored slightly. His impulse was to say "my brother." Whether of high rank or no rank, John of God called all men "brother"—that is, all except churchmen. But what, he wondered, was he to call an archangel?

As if in answer to John's unvoiced question, the Archangel Raphael smiled and said to him, "Brother, we form one and the same Order, for there are men who under a poor garment are equal to the angels. Take this bread which Heavens sends you for your poor."

Scarcely had his helping hand flown back to Heaven before John was flying through night-shelter and wards, calling out jubilantly, "Have courage, my brothers! An angel of God has brought you bread from Heaven!"

These supernatural favors had but one effect on John: they intensified his charity and his sense of nothingness. He could accept them without disturbance to his spirit, for he saw them as favors bestowed solely upon his poor, not upon himself. And it gladdened rather than dismayed him that word of the marvels spread. Patients told the doctors who in turn told their families and friends who in turn told others, and so on, with the result that more and more Granadinos were doing good to themselves, as John begged them to do on his rounds every night. Everything that he needed began to come to him in greater abundance than formerly.

That well-to-do Granadinos were taking an interest in his second hospital and giving generously to its needs was a blessing for which John was deeply grateful. Alms and other necessaries did not, however, change his routine. He could not have worked harder had Granada been stricken by the plague. Tireless in his zeal to aid and console, John of God went from bed to bed, from wards to kitchen, back to the wards, back to the kitchen; to his night-shelter, to the streets. He went in and out of squalid homes where the ailing, the hungry and ragged awaited his attentions

and gifts. Every alley and hovel was known to him; the
porticoes of every public building, the darkest corners
of churches, river banks, bridges and plazas, for in each
and all the sick and destitute lay. A cheerful serenity
concealed his heartache, as well as the piercing, fiery head
pains that would have made any but a saint cry out in
anguish. He labored for the relief of others until he was
ready to drop from exhaustion.

Day and night, John of God moved among the poor.
The poor were his work; the work and the man were one.
John was the charity of Christ incarnate. He could no
more have turned away from a person in need than from
his Savior, and in being always with the poor he was with
his Lord, for in every sufferer he saw the image of Christ
Crucified. Ever striving for greater closeness to God, he
did not know how close God was to him. Then what the
beggarly apostle of charity least expected, happened.

On his way home late one night, John was brought to a
halt by the one sound that claimed his attention before
any other—the moan or cry of one in pain. The street was
narrow and dark, without any light, except at the entrance,
where a single lantern glimmered dimly. All at once, the
cloud that veiled the moon drifted on and a flow of silvery
radiance spilled over a figure crouched against the wall of
a house. A glance told John that the man was poor. He was
dressed in a frayed tunic, his feet were bare and he wore
no cloak or hood.

John leaned over him and asked quietly, "What is it,
brother?"

"I am wounded," came the whispered answer.

Wounded? John's practiced eye studied him. No wound
was visible, no blood. But the grayish pallor, the look of
utter exhaustion were sufficient to cause John anxiety. To

this short-breathed, wayworn pauper, as to all others, he immediately offered his help and his strength. Deftly, he took him in his arms and carried him to his hospital.

Once there, John pursued his usual ritual. Seating the man on a chair in a ward, he knelt before him and bathed his feet. Gently he dried them, then kissed the arch of each foot. Just as he raised his head a little, he gasped and drew back with a start. Impossible! He closed his eyes for an instant, opened them and stared once again. His eyes had not deceived him. Each foot was marked with the sacred wound of the single nail that had fixed them to the Cross. From both blood-colored spots there suddenly issued prismed rays of dazzling light. John's body trembled with his heart's wild pounding. Prostrating himself before Him, he heard the Wounded One say:

"John, John, My faithful servant, be not afraid. I came to thank you for the care you take of My poor. All that you do for them in My Name, you do for Me. I keep count of all your steps and all your journeys in their behalf. I am clothed in the garments with which you cover the needy. It is My feet that you wash, My wounds you dress when you do this to a poor or a sick person. I will be your reward."

Overcome, John might have remained prone on the floor, had not his patients screamed in panic. "Father John, Father John, the ward is on fire! Help us out!" He got up hastily. The chair was empty. The ward was ablaze with a gleaming that was not from the moon which shone in through the windows. Rather was it drenched in a glorious fiery gold. Washed in its radiance, John of God calmly soothed his startled sick, saying, "This fire, my children, is not to consume your bodies nor to destroy our home. All this wonderful brightness is meant to set our hearts aglow with the flames of charity. Our Lord Himself visited you under the guise of a poor and wounded beggar."

Word of this miracle spread far and fast. People who had never gone near John's hospital poured into it now to question the patients, who told and retold the marvel they had seen. Many Granadinos went merely out of curiosity, hoping to catch sight of the impressively humble man who once had chosen to feign madness in order to atone for his sins by the mockery, insults and floggings that inevitably were poured upon such unfortunates, and who now consorted with angels and had bathed the feet of God! People came. People gave. Material assistance grew like smoke from the flame of John's charity. The miracle that supplied him with many needed things for his poor, brought something to John as well: his first experience of spiritual martyrdom.

# NINETEEN

**G**O on, Father Portillo," said John sadly to his confessor. "What more do they have to say against me?"

"Nothing against you personally. Your benefactors deplore your lack of judgment. You make no distinction between one beggar and another."

"How can I? Hunger is hunger. Sickness is sickness."

"Yes," admitted the priest, "but not all who come to you are unable to help themselves. Do you question their sincerity? Never. Do you question them at all? You do not. You merely respond to whatever is wanted." Father Portillo watched the thin, tormented face opposite him. He knew that John could not help responding to the needs of others. Virtuous himself, he saw good in all men. He did not choose from among the many who appealed to him, but gave to each and all, and in this lay the reason for the outcry against him.

His face drawn with anxiety, his hands clasped together, he asked, "What am I supposed to do, Father? Close my hospital? Give up my work?"

"You're being more emotional than sensible, John. To some extent, you will have to compromise."

Compromise! The word stung. "Compromise my conscience, my heart, my eternal salvation? I cannot. Tell me, Father, is some of this criticism directed at the girls and women I have provided for?"

"Possibly," replied the priest.

John reflected in silence. Maria Paz was a closed chapter in his life, yet she had never quite left it. He had but to see a young girl to be reminded of her purity, her charm, her piety. She remained the ideal that he wanted every girl and young woman to be like. With a portion of the alms that had come to him recently, he had obtained a suitable house to which he could take girls without family or home, and over whom he placed motherly widows whose morals were beyond reproach. Daily he visited the house, prayed with his charges, made them little sermons and encouraged industry, for he wished them to become useful and self-sustaining. He himself taught them to sew and spin. In return, he asked only devotion to God, devotion to work and cleanliness.

"The foundlings," he said suddenly, with a trace of bitterness that was tinged with sorrow. "Is the world afraid of forsaken babies, too? I take great pains to find good foster parents for them and to make certain they will be brought up in an atmosphere of piety."

"There is one child in particular—" began Father Portillo. He was interrupted by John. "Yes, Father, there is. She is a year old now, a beautiful baby and," he admitted, with a slow smile, "of them all, she is my favorite. If you have heard that once a week I walk to the farm in the Vega to see her, the rumor is true. I love that little girl," he said with charming simplicity. "It is also true that I give what money I can to the kindly people who adopt these children, and I am trying to save up enough to give a dowry to each baby girl— and to the other girls as well."

"That's one of the complaints, John. There are those who are not sympathetic to the notion of their money be-

ing spent on girls you find in the streets and on foundlings
that are left at your door and God alone knows where else."

Quickly and hotly, John replied, "I have put their con-
tributions to good use. Surely you are not asking me to
turn those girls and widows out into the streets again, or
to cease to do what I can for the families who take the
foundlings?"

"Not for a moment, John. I encourage this charity. If
you'd forget about the dowries, that might mollify your
benefactors."

"I'll mollify no one in that way. You know as well as I
that, without a dowry, a girl cannot make a decent marriage. If the benefactors prefer to withdraw their aid, that
is their privilege. With God's help, I will find the means
to support my poor."

Father Portillo smiled gloomily. "In the main," he said,
"you are accused of taking into your hospital and shelter
men and youths who have given scandal by their behavior
and who are undeserving of your charity which is made
possible by the generosity of others."

"I am not aware of anyone who is undeserving of my
help. If there are bad men among them, can they not be
redeemed?"

"They can be. But are they?"

"I don't know, I don't know. I only know that, if I reject them, they may really rebel against God, and then
their sins will be upon my soul."

"No, John, no! It is better to turn away uncouth men
than to sully the reputation of your hospital. Moreover,
you must look ahead. You have two hundred beds in your
hospital now, and if you had twice the number, you still
would not have enough. Before long, you'll need larger
quarters. You cannot afford to aggravate your benefactors.

If you lose their support, it will not be their fault entirely."
Father Portillo waited for John to agree. But the latter was
silent. He was filled with a sense of futility and failure.
The pain was in his head again, darting, burning, and
there was the prick of tears behind his eyes. Unaware of
the gesture, he pressed his hands hard against the sides of
his head. "I know," said the priest, with sympathy, "it
hits you over the head when you are accused of being too
kind. For you, compassion is a cross." He saw John lean
his head on his hands, to hide his eyes.

Torn between the desire to obey and to give help to any
and all, John said at last, "Believe me, Father, I trust the
wisdom of your counsel. However, with your permission,
I should like to have the opinion of Father John of Avila.
Would you mind?"

"Of course I wouldn't. He is your spiritual director.
Write to him."

John wrote.

The spiritual master of saints replied at once.

"Do as Father Portillo tells you," he wrote. "If you followed your own thinking, I should have reason to fear. A
great saint has said that he who listens only to himself does
not need the devil to ruin him. Very often we believe we
are right, then we fall into difficulties. Continue to obey
Father Portillo. Do not admit quarrelsome, cursing, ill-
behaved men to your hospital. They will but bring it into
disrepute. Never feel that to turn away an unworthy person is to be wanting in charity. Know sometimes how to
refuse what is asked of you, learn how to say no, and expel
from your hospital any who set a bad example. God has
not given you the vocation to direct, but to be directed.
Therefore, obey Father Portillo as you would obey
me . . ."

John's thoughts no longer veered, except in the direction that his confessor had pointed out for him. His obedience to Father Portillo's advice was perfect, though not without pain to himself. For most men, the harshest hairshirt consists in learning to love the unloved; the cruelest penance for John of God was to deny them his love. Outside his hospital, he could give it without restrictions, and in the streets he dispensed charity with reckless and happy abandon. Long before the day was over, John had little left to give, except his tunic. Rare was the day that he left home and returned wearing the same one. Invariably, he exchanged his for one more ragged than his own.

Against him or for him, there was scarcely a Granadino who had not heard of him. There were still some few who had not seen him. Among these was Don Sebastian Ramírez y Fuenleal, Bishop of Tuy and President of the Royal Chamber of Granada. He sent a special message to John, saying that he wished to see him, so John of God set forth to keep the appointment. Somewhere along the way he met a beggar, and, as always happened, the beggar's shift was poorer than John's. The Bishop made no attempt to conceal his surprise when the famous Father of the Poor appeared before him in perhaps the worst-looking outfit anybody had ever seen him wearing.

John knelt to kiss the Bishop's ring, then stood before him. His tall figure seemed to fill the small, plainly furnished room which was the Bishop's private study, and where he saw those with whom he wished to speak in utmost confidence. Don Sebastian hesitated for a second. John's height and wonderful face, the luminous quality of his eyes, of his whole presence, amazed the Bishop as much as the tattered garment that hung on the gaunt but powerful frame.

So this was the great apostle of charity! Here was the man who lifted up the poor in spirit, the remarkable Christian who lived his belief that, if one loves and serves God, one must also love and serve God's image in man. This majestic shadow was he whose name, when mentioned to almost anyone at all, immediately produced a word picture of a towering, barefoot saint with a basket strapped to his back, kettle handles looped over the crooks of his elbows, his arms bearing a sick person, supporting the crippled or leading the blind. Frequently, too, he was seen hurrying through the streets to his hospital, a whimpering foundling pressed to his breast.

Giving himself a little shake, Don Sebastian came out of his musings, motioned John to take the chair on the other side of the table that held a standing crucifix, writing paper, quills, inkpot, scarlet sealing wax, a silver sand-caster and a pale candle in a gilded holder. In as natural a voice as he could manage, the Bishop said, "For some time I have wanted to meet you. I am told that you are a rarity, a man of ideas, one who thinks for himself but never of himself."

John shook his head vigorously. "If I have ideas, Your Lordship, I have them only by the grace of God. I am an empty-headed, unlearned man. I am nothing." There was no false modesty in this statement. Don Sebastian recognized it for what it was: the honest sentiment of a man striving to free himself of self, to become total nothing-ness, knowing that in nothingness God will be all to the soul.

"Your hospital," continued the Bishop, "has achieved fame on numerous counts. For the reforms and methods which you have introduced, Granada is indebted to you."

"Granada is indebted to God," declared John. "Let Granada give thanks to Him. It is God who gives a man thoughts and skill, and He alone can cure or not, according to His will. As for my methods—" John smiled and his smile was strong and gentle, "they amount to little more than a poor imitation of Our Lord's love. Practically speaking, anybody can do what I do. Let in air and sunshine, create a cheerful atmosphere, segregate diseases, boil everything, serve nourishing food and encourage rest and sleep. Experience has taught me that mental cases ought not to be starved, kept in dark and filthy cells, prevented from sleeping and beaten half to death. Demonic possession is not the cause of madness, I am positive of that. Nor is cruelty the cure. What is at the root of insanity? I do not know."

Neither did he know that he perceived, by the gift of grace, what many doctors had not learned from books or patients. In the strict hygiene that was applied to every detail in his hospital, and in his handling of the insane, John of God was divinely inspired and centuries ahead of his day. The brutal treatment that he condemned in the sixteenth century was continued into the nineteenth. Shakespeare, in the seventeenth century, upheld the merciless manner of dealing with the insane, when he put into the mouth of one of his characters the common sentiment that a lunatic deserved a dark house and the whip. During this same century, the voice of a German physician was heard to advocate regular beatings for the insane, in the belief that lashing "cleared the brain and braced the nerves." England, medically far behind Spain even in the sixteenth century, was still unenlightened in the nineteenth. In the year 1810, Sir Thomas More, the author of *Utopia,* the classic that describes an imaginary island

where life is ideal and perfect, gave his support to the
view that the insane were best served by being flogged, not
in private but in public. Not even King George III, who
suffered a mental disorder, was exempted. He, too, was
whipped in a public place in the presence of his subjects.
Esteemed as one of the great humanitarians of all time, it
is doubtful whether Sir Thomas More ever heard of the
humble and humane Saint John of God. Six years after
More's endorsement of public flogging for the deranged,
there came to the world's notice an eminent physician
and true humanitarian in France. Large-hearted and fearless, Philippe Pinel followed the example of John of God.
With a kind of holy wrath, he struck off the chains that
pinned the mad to the musty holes they were imprisoned
in, and flung away the lash.

For a long while, Don Sebastian engaged John in talk
pertaining to his hospital and his work among the poor
of Granada. Finally, he asked, "Were you born in
Granada?"

"No, Your Lordship, I was born in Montemor-o-Novo,
in Portugal."

"You are new to Spain?"

"Oh, no, I have lived here many years."

There was, for an instant, a strangely knowing look in
the Bishop's face. In a voice that was admiring and kind,
he said, "You are loved and known as the Father of the
Poor, the Apostle of Charity. Your baptismal name is John,
that much I know."

John began to fidget with one of the quills that lay in
a small tray on the table. He seemed to anticipate a question that he would rather not be asked.

"What is your full name?"

"John Ciudad y Duarte, Your Lordship." Without looking up, he added, "In Portuguese, *Cidade*." Feeling the other's eyes fixed intently upon him, John colored a little.

"And your true name?" pressed the Bishop.

At this, John glanced at him and eyed him with wonder. Don Sebastian smiled. "I myself cannot say why I asked that question. Intuition, perhaps. But I am not mistaken, am I?"

"No, Your Lordship." John wished fervently that intuition had not touched the Bishop. He sighed. Still toying with the quill, he said, "I have no secrets from you, *Ilustrisimo*. A little Boy came to me in a wood one day. I believe He was the Child Jesus. In the palm of His hand He held an open pomegranate, and from the crown of the fruit there rose a small cross of gold. He said to me: *John of God, Granada will be your cross.* Then he vanished in a golden mist of light."

"John of God," echoed the Bishop, slowly. "A name from Heaven."

"It ought not to be mine," said John. "I cannot believe that it is."

"It is your name." The Bishop was convinced. To himself he thought, Long after you are dead, John of God, men will call out that name, men will remember. But when he spoke now, his tone was matter-of-fact. "You conceal it. Why?"

"Your Lordship, how can I do otherwise? I am a sinner. I am unworthy of the name. Not until now have I revealed it to anyone except Father John of Avila."

"Did he not tell you to use it?"

"No, Your Lordship."

"Then I shall."

John caught his breath in a gasp of fright. "Please, Your Lordship, please do not put me under obedience to use it. For me to go under that name would be a betrayal of all that is perfect and beautiful."

"Not to use it," countered Don Sebastian, "is the only betrayal. You go scarlet at the thought of bearing a name which Our Lord Himself has given you! A glorious name, a most singular favor! God is charity. He who is *of God* has a mission of charity. Would you disown the Master Whom you serve?"

There was horror in John's eyes. "No, no, no, never, Your Lordship, never! But I am not worthy," he protested desperately. "I am a man of no account. You can see for yourself what I am."

Don Sebastian smiled. "I can see that you need a new garment."

Again John gasped and took a quick look at the rags he was wearing.

"That shift," said the Bishop, "no doubt is congenial to your humility, but it's hardly suitable."

"Why is it unsuitable?" John asked meekly.

"It isn't proper to your profession of nurse and protector of the poor, and it is ill-suited to the dignity of your name."

"Surely Your Lordship would not have me go among my poor dressed up like a grandee!"

"I surely would not. I hadn't entertained such an idea. No, nothing in the way of splendor. Merely a garment that would make you look more respectable."

"This shift is threadbare," John conceded, "but I find it quite respectable."

"Well, it may seem so to you. I am thinking of the public. People judge by appearances. They shouldn't; nevertheless they do."

"But in the end, Your Lordship, it is God Who judges

us, not people. What will count with Him—the way I am
dressed or the way I try to keep His Commandments?"

"In your case," said the Bishop, stifling a smile, "what
will really count is your obedience to Grace—and to
Bishops." After a moment he said, seriously, "I understand
you, my son. Still, you cannot get around it: you need the
alms and services of the rich. Human nature being what it
is, people will be more disposed to generosity if you are
decently attired than if you aren't." Without more ado, he
took a small silver bell from the table drawer and rang it.
A servant came running. "Send in the master of the wardrobe," ordered Don Sebastian.

John sat silent in misery.

A faint smile played about the Bishop's lips as he took
paper, quill and ink and drew a design of the garment he
wanted for John. Between pen strokes, he darted amused
looks at his guest and marveled at his self-control. He was
bound to be curious, the Bishop was thinking, yet he kept
his gaze on the floor, as though the sketch were a confi-
dential letter that he'd no business glancing at.

Presently, in came the wardrobe master. He took John's
measurements, examined the Bishop's sketch and consulted with him in low tones. "There's nothing to it, Your
Lordship. A straight, plain tunic with wide sleeves and
a cincture. That's all?"

"That's all. Use a rough-textured cloth. Dark gray."

"Yes, Your Lordship. It won't take long."

"Fine!" Don Sebastian beamed. "The sooner I get him
into it, the better."

"Oh? He's to wear it at once?" The master shot a somewhat haughty look at the sad-faced giant in tatters.

"At once. As for you, consider it a high compliment that
the task is yours to make it for him. Now, get on with it."

The master returned in record time. Don Sebastian took the garment, dismissed him, blessed the cloth and gave it to John. "This is no ordinary tunic, John of God. It is a habit."

John stood by, puzzled. "I am a layman, Your Lordship. I cannot wear a habit."

"You can and you shall. Get out of that shift and into this habit. You are not the only layman who does God's work in the world without belonging to the world. Henceforth, you are to wear this habit, or one made exactly like it. In no circumstances," he said with severity, "are you to give this consecrated habit to a beggar in return for rags." Don Sebastian stood watching him. John's lean, well-built body could not have been more prepossessing had it been attired in splendor. "Does it meet with your approval?"

"Your Lordship, I love it very much, and I give you my word that I will revere it for the blessing which you have put upon it." He paused . . . "May I ask a favor?"

Don Sebastian nodded.

"If I am asked my name," John said, "I promise to give it. But I would be most grateful not to be under obedience to use it otherwise. It is written on my heart. Let me keep it there."

The Bishop agreed to this. He wondered a moment. "Do you correspond with Father John of Avila?"

"Yes, Your Lordship."

"With anyone else?"

"I send letters of thanks to my benefactors."

"By what name do you sign them?"

"John," he answered. "Or, more often, Brother John." He laughed a little. "My poor call me Father. I call them Brother and sign myself Brother. Religiously speaking, I am neither priest nor brother. I truly am nothing. I ought simply to use the cipher that stands for zero."

"Who would know what the cipher signifies? No," said the Bishop, "you'll have to do better than that."

John looked at him, smiling. "I have it, Your Lordship. *Yo Fray Cero.* I Brother Zero."

"At least it's original," the Bishop allowed slowly. He was tempted to say: *Yo Fray Santo.* I Brother Saint. But he kept the thought to himself. "Well, Brother Zero, now you have a habit and a name. What next? Disciples?"

"Disciples? Followers?" John shook his head. "I have a few former patients staying with me. For them, it means a home; for me, it means help with kitchen work, scrubbing floors, laundry, that kind of thing. But no one as yet has shown any inclination to give himself to the poor and the sick in the way that I would demand."

"God will take care of that in His own good time, Brother Zero. We are disposed to rush things. Where's the use? God won't be pushed."

"Actually," John decided, a light note in his voice, "I wouldn't know what to do or where to begin if a candidate presented himself."

"You can always come to me. I may have a suggestion or two. If nothing else, I can provide him with a tunic like your own." Don Sebastian gave John's arm a briskly affectionate pat. "No need to worry now. First get the follower."

John of God's memorable visit with the Bishop of Tuy was still uppermost in his mind when everybody else in Granada was thinking and talking of nothing except the bitter rift between two friends. The one had charged the other with the murder of his brother and was living for the day when he'd see him hanged on the scaffold. Two men less like John of God could scarcely be imagined.

# TWENTY

KNEELING by the bedside of an elderly and very sick man, John of God gazed with profound tenderness at the wasted face on the pillow and touched the crucifix to the colorless lips. From his own lips came a soothing flow of words, such as a brave but saddened father might speak to a hopelessly sick child. "Do not be afraid, brother," he murmured. "Our Lord will give us eternal glory through the merits of His Sacred Passion. The most wonderful thing in the world is that God sent His Divine Son to live among men for a few years. He lived. He died. He lives again, and we who love and keep His laws shall live with and in Him forever. Think only of Our Lord's mercy and cling to the hand of Our Lady and Mother."

"There is only one man in Granada who can relieve the dying of fear that way—the only one I know whose charges never leave this world with even a hint of terror." Dr. Pedro Raxis spoke in a low tone, more to himself than to John, who would not have known he was there, except that the soft rustle of the physician's scarlet gown drew his attention. Gently he released the dying man's fingers from his own and got to his feet.

"Did you send for Father Peralta?"

"Yes, Vicente raced out to fetch him. He'll get here in time." Doctor Raxis glanced at the patient. "He's sleeping," he said. "Completely at peace." And once again he spoke as to himself. "Love is the answer. That's what you give them, John. Love. Love is your religion."

"God is my religion, Doctor, and God is love. I try to give them God, Who gave Himself on the Cross for us." Charity, sacrifice and love. Is that too much to give for eternal salvation?"

"For you," said the Doctor, "it is a great price. To take the terror out of death for others takes too much out of you. Unless you give a thought to yourself now and again, you'll be the next to go." Doctor Raxis regarded John with admiration and anxiety in one. "You're carrying not only the biggest but the most sorrowful kind of burden."

"Sorrowful, yes, but not big. In any case, it is the one that God wants me to carry. This is my life," John stated simply, "and I thank God for it."

"So do I, John; so does every doctor who serves your poor. But we worry about you."

"Oh, you doctors!" John tried to smile.

"Ignore us. We cannot ignore you." Dr. Raxis paused, thought to himself: Was there ever a man who walked up to every kind of misery and affliction with outstretched arms like this one? Dedicated to his vocation as nurse, protector and consoler, John of God could pour affection and faith over everyone he encountered. They came from him like a cataract of light. Every poor person in need looked to him for help and none was refused save those whom Father Portillo judged unworthy. In his immense charity, as well as in his obedience, John of God was a pure, clear echo of his divine Lord. Pulling himself back to the moment, Dr. Raxis said, "You work incessantly, eat nothing, and I question whether you truly sleep the one hour that you say you do."

His eyes on the still face on the pillow, John replied

tranquilly, "One way or another, Doctor, one has to pay
for the blessings that God sends. The sick poor are mine."

The other wanted to say: Anyone fortunate enough to
have your care is especially blessed. He asked instead,
"Have you had spells of faintness again?"

"I'm well enough. You mustn't worry about me."

"I might not, if I hadn't eyes and ears. This work is
taking its toll of you, John. The emotional strain on you
is perhaps even worse. You can evade my questions but
you can't hide your heart from me. Nor the sobs that
sometimes rack your body. I've seen you," he said, "when
you thought you were hidden and alone. I know the
corners you retire to when you cannot endure to see another's pain for a single second." He stopped, took John
by the arm. "Come along. Let's go to the kitchen. You can
give me a cup of broth, though you are the one who should
take it. Father Peralta should be here at any moment. You
and I have done all that we can." Dr. Raxis looked at the
patient. "The end will be peaceful," he said. "Sometimes,
John, I think God created these poor destitute sick in
order to make them the recipients of your love, which is
His own. They are to be envied. Even the incurables are a
thousand times better off than men like Anthony Martin
and Peter Velasco." Firmly, the doctor led John out of the
ward and toward the kitchen, the only place in the hospital
where a person could talk with Brother Zero privately, for,
since he had added seventy-five beds to the original one
hundred and twenty-five, every inch of space was given
over to the sick. He had no room of his own in his first
little hospital on the *Calle de Lucena,* nor had he a cell in
his second. Here, as at the other, he slept on the stones,
under the stairway.

"Are there further developments?" John asked, as he

ladled broth into a glazed brown bowl and set it before the
Doctor.

"In the Martin-Velasco case? No, Martin still wants the
death sentence for Velasco and Velasco wants eternal hell-
fire for Martin. He swears that he is innocent of murder."

"Does he deny having killed Martin's brother?"

The doctor swallowed a spoonful of broth and shook his
head. "He stoutly denies it. They fought over some matter of no consequence. Merely as a threat, Velasco claims,
he drew his dagger. The other tried to wrest it from his
grasp and twisted Velasco's hand in such a way as to accidentally stab himself through the heart. Nothing less
than a miracle of grace will save the life of the one and
the soul of the other. I am acquainted with friends of
Anthony Martin. They say they scarcely recognize him, he
has changed so greatly. He is consumed with bitterness
and vengeance and is not to be reasoned with. The trial is
lagging. While he waits for the proceedings to get under-
way, he spends his time and money at dicing and drink-
ing."

"Not all of it," said John. "He isn't as bad as you think."

"Bad enough," the Doctor commented dryly.

"I daresay he is stubborn and quick-tempered. So am I."
John threw a handful of dry faggots on the fire, then charcoal, and then placed a heavy iron on the embers, prepar-
ing to press the linen for the entire hospital. "He may also
be over-conscious of his Spanish honor," John continued.
"Honor and pride demand of him that his brother's death
be avenged. Pride will get him nowhere. He will discover
that for himself." John looked Dr. Raxis fully in the eyes
and declared, "I like Anthony Martin, I like him very
much." His sincerity was so obvious that the other stared
at him, bewildered. "Why shouldn't I? I never pass him

in the streets but he opens his purse and pours gold into my hands. Last week," John said, returning from a cupboard with a stack of washed, unironed towels, "he came here to offer a large donation."

"And you took it?"

"Certainly, Doctor. I need every coin that I can get."

"Aren't you supposed to exercise scruples where men who give scandal are concerned?"

"I am. I do. But nobody has said that I am not to take alms. Anthony is a generous man, I assure you, and what he offers, I accept."

"Even though he is disguising evil under the gleam of gold?"

"He isn't evil." John picked up the iron, tested the flat of it with a drop of water. It didn't hiss, so he replaced it on the embers. "Nor can evil come of almsgiving, only good. *Shut up alms in the heart of the poor, and it shall obtain help for thee against all evil.* That is what Holy Scripture tells us. You'll find it in *Ecclesiasticus,* Chapter Twenty-nine."

The doctor's eyes lingered on John's serene face with a look that mingled pity and puzzlement. "On the one hand," he said, "you are counting on almsgiving to save him; on the other, you are eating your heart out for him, afraid that nothing will save him. Admit it."

"I am not as hopeless as all that, Doctor. God is bound to soften his hardness regarding Velasco."

"Why so?"

The reply came with simplicity. "He is kind. He has helped my poor. I love him and grieve for him, and if I do, surely Our Lord must, for His mercy is infinite."

There was silence. John gazed dreamily into space, as unaware of the doctor as if he were not present. Peter

Raxis took advantage of his companion's withdrawal into solitude. Having a flair for art and having often asked John to pose for him, only to be refused, he took paper from the leather pouch that contained instruments, pellets and powders, then took a stick of charcoal from the copper pen case that hung at his belt. Deftly he sketched the face of John of God, which at this instant, it seemed to him, had in its expression all the profound love and sorrow of which the Father of the Poor was capable. He caught the sad reflectiveness in the beautiful eyes, the gentleness and strength of his elusive personality. Later, he was to use this sketch as a model for an oil portrait, the only one known to have been made of the saint during his lifetime.

"If he dices and drinks and gives scandal," said John, after a while, "it is because he is tormented. Never mind, God has His own way of curing pride. His most effective weapon is suffering. You say," he reminded the doctor without looking at him, "that he hasn't responded to argument. Then I say the arguments were not sympathetic. He needs a friend; he needs understanding. Somebody should go to him and—" John broke off without saying what should be done. But there was a shining in his eyes that said more than words. In haste, he removed the iron from the coals and stood it on the brick floor. "I'll do the linen later. Oh, would you kindly see if Father Peralta has come? If he wasn't available, send for Father Portillo. Please excuse me, Doctor."

"If anyone asks, where shall I say you have gone?"

"To the house of Anthony Martin."

John did not have to go that far. He soon came upon Anthony, wandering about in the market square, tossing coins into the tambourines of gypsy women. Immediately he reached him, John sank to his knees at Anthony's feet. "Please," he began, "Anthony, please—"

"With pleasure, Father John. Here, take it all." He handed over his money bag, saw the gray-habited man shake his head. "It isn't alms you want? What then? How can I help you?"

"By helping yourself. Pardon Peter Velasco."

"*Pardon?*" Anthony stared at him, incredulous, and again he repeated, "*Pardon?* What do you take me for? An idiot? A man without honor?"

"No, I take you for a good man, worthy of salvation. As for honor, there is no honor in what you are doing to Velasco."

"Was there honor in him when he murdered my brother?"

"He did not murder him. He has taken an oath on that."

"An oath won't bring my brother back," returned Anthony with bitterness.

"Neither will the death of Peter Velasco. Anthony, if you persist in rejecting his oath as false, if you are determined to demand his life's blood, do not look to God to pardon you your sins."

Anthony's face reddened. His lips curled in a derisive smile. "Why should Peter Velasco be spared?" He shouted the question at John and at the onlookers who had gathered around them. "He took a life; let him pay with his own. Pardon him! By all the saints, Father John, you say that as if it were a small matter. Ask me anything but that. You can take my purse or my house, but not my right to see Velasco hanged."

"If your brother's death was accidental, and I am convinced that it was, then it is not your right to see Velasco hanged. Even if it hadn't been an accident, I would beg you to pardon him."

"It's plain that you don't know Velasco."

It was plain to John that he could not show sympathy for Anthony's afflicted spirit. He replied, "I know him well enough to realize that he is not a murderer. Destroy him, and you will never have a moment's peace again. You cannot escape the effects. Velasco is your friend."

"*Was* my friend," Anthony snapped.

"The day may come," John warned him, "when Our Lord will say the same of you." Suddenly, John withdrew his crucifix from the inside of his sleeve, kissed it, clasped it in both hands and held it up to Anthony. "Look at your Lord. Think a little of His agony. To imagine the depths of it is impossible. No trial that He sends us is comparable to what He suffered for our redemption. In one day, Anthony, I see more anguish of body and soul than you may have seen in all your life. Yet all of it together, the world over, cannot compare to one second of Our Lord's Passion and Crucifixion. It is human not to want sickness and grief, I know that. I am surrounded by those for whom there is almost no hope of anything else. They know it. They also know the one thing that you seem to have forgotten."

Anthony did not ask what. Sullen, unyielding, his eyes were like two blue-gray stones. His look said that, if he had been faced by any other than John of God, he would have walked away long since.

"They know," John continued, "that nothing is necessary to them except God. They accept their crosses with courage. Not ever have I heard any one of them ask, 'Why does God do this to me?' "

"I haven't said that," protested Anthony.

"Perhaps not in those words. Yet every time you cry out

for Velasco's life, you say it." John looked up at him sadly. "You would do better to read the Passion according to Saint John than to spend your time in wineshops. You'll find no solace until you forgive Velasco and accept your cross with good grace. Continue to offend Our Lord, and you will lose your cross. Then you'll be bereft of far more than a brother. I have done nothing for you; yet to me you have given much. Our Lord died for you. Can you not offer to Him the pardon of your friend?"

Anthony was silent.

"I have wept over you, Anthony."

"Why should you?"

"Because Hell is Hell. It exists. If only," John pleaded, "if only you would meditate a little on God's love and mercy!"

"And if I did, what then?" demanded Anthony coldly.

"You would want to do good, all the good possible for as long as you are able. None of us knows when his hour will come. But we know that as we shall be found, so shall we be judged. Please, Anthony, please! Ask God's forgiveness of your sins in return for your pardon of Peter Velasco."

Anthony Martin was only dimly conscious of the spectators, who breathed sighs of relief when he dropped to his knees in front of John.

"You have forced a hard choice upon me," he said, "but I thank you for it. I will withdraw the charges against Velasco. I will even be his friend, if you will do something for me. Help me to save my soul with the same zeal with which you have saved the life of Peter Velasco."

John's strong hands gripped Anthony's shoulders. "All is well. Do not be afraid." Brother Zero stood. The other got to his feet. Looming over him, John caught the strange gaze that Anthony gave him. "Come now, it takes no great courage to go to an imprisoned friend and say to him that he soon will be free of an unjust accusation which you, in blind rage, made against him. Say to him that you intend to drop the charge against him and to ask that the case be dismissed, for now you realize that he spoke the truth when he testified on oath that, although he drew his dagger, not to kill but to threaten, it was your brother who accidentally stabbed himself while trying to wrest the weapon from Peter's grip. Why do you hesitate? Is it your pride?"

"No, not that. If I go alone, Peter will not believe a word that I say to him, nor can I blame him. He'll think it is a deceit, a trick of some sort."

"I see. One of you will argue the other into a temper." John's grim face brightened into a smile. "Then I'd better go with you. But you, Anthony, must be the one to tell him. I'll stand by and uphold the facts, if he doubts you." Brother Zero paused, caught and held the steadfast gaze of the other. "You owe yourself another kindness. Beg Velasco's pardon for not believing him when he spoke the truth. Will you?"

"Yes, I will."

"Thank you." John was grateful and happy. He addressed God silently but with fervor, looking suddenly less tired and much younger. "Come, let us go to him at once," he urged, and put his arm around the shoulders of the chastened young man, like an older brother.

After a moment, Anthony asked awkwardly, "May I ask, do you need, could you use . . . ?" He longed to say what was in his heart but could not.

"Whatever you have in mind, the answer is yes. I need and can use simply everything."

"Even a sinner? One who'd like to spend the rest of his life with you, serving the sick and the poor? Do you trust me?"

"I trust you, but——." Although John understood what Anthony was getting at, he stifled his excitement by pretending to doubt the man's fitness for this kind of service. "When I ran into you a while ago, you were strolling through the marketplace. He who shares my lot will never have time for idle walks. You're robust, perfectly able to work. The point is, will you? And will you love it? Without love, it's no use. You were not brought up to work. Few Spaniards accept work for what it is—a shining facet in the jewel that is Christian living. They forget that Our Lord said: *My Father works, and I work.*" John threw a searching glance at the pensive Anthony and smiled to himself. "Have you zeal for the sick and the poor? Would you be able to show tenderness toward any and all without exception and not be tempted to choose the one with the least disgusting disease, or the cleanest, or the best-mannered? Have you charity, always charity?"

"Obviously not always," Anthony admitted. He sighed, discouraged. "I suppose I haven't much of anything, really, except a good intention. That is not enough, is it?"

John's hand tightened on Anthony's shoulder for a second. The reassuring gesture answered Anthony more eloquently than words. A good intention was enough when fortified with grace. John could not doubt that grace had flowed from God to this repentant man, as warmth flows from the sun. He knew perfectly well that Anthony Martin was bodily and spiritually fit for the life he wished to embrace. But he had wanted Anthony to give thought to the requisites which he himself deemed essential, and which henceforth he was to recommend for contemplation to others who might desire to join him in his work. What he had said to Anthony summed up, in brief, the basic characteristics that John looked for in those who wished to care for the sick and the needy: health, fervor for work, love for this particular kind of work, zeal for the infirm and the poor, tenderness toward all without exception and the charity of Christ Himself.

Anthony Martin was to become his first follower; of that John was sure. But the thought never crossed his mind that this miracle of grace was to be repeated, with similar suddenness and spontaneity, in the soul of Peter Velasco, who at this moment sat hunched against a wall of his prison cell, brooding bitterly. Presently, however, Anthony and Peter, formerly friends, lately enemies, were to confront one another. Unbelieving at first, Peter reacted exactly as Anthony feared he would. Gradually, however, his stubborn refusal to take the other at his word began to soften. Quite suddenly, he lowered his eyes and said no more. For a long moment he pondered John of God's quiet insistence that he, John, would not be party to deception, that no matter how surprising Anthony's change of heart might seem, the change was a fact. Anthony, John had said, meant every word he had spoken; he was sincere in his determination to obtain the release of his friend at the soonest possible moment. He was equally sincere in having begged his, Peter's, forgiveness for having appealed the case which, after one trial had found Peter innocent. Having meant all of it wholeheartedly, Peter, in turn, must believe Anthony wholeheartedly. So Peter reasoned that, if John of God was convinced, there was nothing to be gained in contradicting him. Neither was there any turning away from the pleading look in John of God's eyes. Who could resist their hypnotic entreaty to do what was right? Well and good, put an end to this senseless hatred. That was that. As had Anthony Martin before him, Peter Velasco surrendered to the power of charity as exemplified in Brother Zero.

When, finally, John and Anthony left the prison, John walked along as in a dream. They hardly spoke. Now that it was over, neither one could think of anything to say. John was on his way home, and had not even suggested that Anthony should go with him. He didn't have to. Already, Anthony was bound to him. It was to be only a matter of days before Peter, who had been seized with the same desire that had attached Anthony to John of God, would present himself to the peacemaker as the second of his first two followers.

# TWENTY
# ONE

JOHN of God was shredding cabbage for the thin soup that again would be the main meal of the day for his growing congregation of Brothers, when Brother Anthony Martin came into the kitchen. Casually, as if he hoped John wouldn't notice, he laid a pile of folded papers at one end of the table.

"What are those, Anthony?"

"Bills, Father. Unpaid." For a moment Anthony watched the blue light that ran along the edge of the steel knife that flashed in John's hand. "I wish I could take that blade to them. Columns and columns of figures."

"And the sum total?" John asked him.

"The sum total," came the prompt reply, "adds up to sore distress in an overcrowded hospital already suffering in the extreme."

"You are worried, Anthony?"

"Yes, I am. We Brothers can go without. But when a hospital is without funds or credit, it is the patients who suffer."

If John was worried, he gave no hint of it. "Don't fret, Anthony. God will take care of His poor. We must beg harder and pray harder for them."

"In the meantime, it is serious to be in want of everything," Anthony reminded him.

"Not quite everything. As time passes, our greatest need of all is being filled. While our creditors justly take from us all that we receive in alms, God in His goodness adds to our numbers. I am satisfied."

"You always are. Just the same, it would help," said Anthony, "if He would add one follower with a fortune at his disposal."

John smiled. "It's as bad as that?"

"At the very least, it's odd that He doesn't."

"What's odd about it?"

"Rather ask what isn't." Anthony became meditative. "Most religious orders attract a few propertied men. We don't."

"We aren't an order, Anthony. We merely live and work and pray together as though we were. We have the hardships without the benefits of an established rule of religious life. Someday perhaps—" John broke off. To himself he said: You will live to see that day. I won't.

"Established or not, if God doesn't assist us through someone, or something, how will we go on? I had a little. Piola had more. Neither of us had enough to make any real difference." Anthony looked at his mentor as at a saint. He had never seen humility and faith equal to those constantly displayed by John of God. "No one but yourself would have accepted the likes of us. For one thing, we came to you almost empty-handed; for another, you had to re-form and convert us; in four instances it required a miracle. Peter and I, your first two, deserved to be known as criminals. Simon of Avila maligned you evilly. Piola was a miser, so wedded to his money that, when you were in dire need, he wouldn't lend you thirty miserable ducats without a pledge against the loan. The security that you showed him had him shivering from head to foot."

John was not listening. His back was turned to Anthony. Having set the cauldron of soup on the fire, he was vigorously scrubbing empty cupboards. Anthony could not take his eyes from John's left arm. Concealed inside the sleeve of his gray habit was the security that had made the beads of perspiration turn cold on Piola's over-heated flesh. Even now, his heartbeat quickened at the thought of the crucifix that had struck terror in the miser's soul, when, from the carved Christ, there had issued rays of unearthly light.

Musing, Anthony said, "Peter the Sinner, Anthony the Sinner, Simon the Sinner, Piola the Beggar. Such titles, I suspect, do not attract dukes and grandees. Any suggestions, Father John?"

"For what?"

"For empty cupboards. How and with what will we fill them?"

"By and with charity."

"We give it, but from whom will we get it in order to give it?"

John looked over his shoulder and smiled at his questioner. "Use your imagination."

"I can't. I've overtaxed it already."

"Then get to work. Take the bills with you. Keep them in a safe place. They'll be paid, little by little—or all at once."

Brother Anthony nodded dazedly and left John to his seemingly endless scrubbing of cupboards and shelves. He shook his head as though to clear it and looked hopelessly at Brother Peter, who was standing in the passageway. "What happened, Anthony?"

"Nothing."

"Maybe you ought not to have burdened him with those bills."

"We're the burdened. He's only mystified as to why we worry."

"Apart from begging," said Brother Peter, "is there a single recourse left to us? Did anything suggest itself to Father John?"

" 'Beg harder and pray harder,' that's all he said."

"Doesn't he realize that we're desperate for food, medicines, oils, linens, clothing and alms? We need them now, this minute. What are we going to do?"

"Only what he says: beg and pray." Staring at the bills in his hand, Anthony reflected, "Ever since the day that he reconciled us, Peter—and that was a miracle of grace— there have been other miracles wrought through him, externally visible ones. Afterward, there was an appreciable change in our circumstances. In each case, you will recall, people were moved to give, give, give. Then, when the wonder wore off, purse strings were drawn tight once more. You ask is there a single recourse left to us. Yes, God. Always there is God. Our present plight may be His way of warning us that we ought to try harder to imitate the example of our Father John, who thinks he is nothing and becomes more and more. As though they were the most precious gifts, he places all his concerns in the hands of the Blessed Mother and her Divine Son. I have known trusting souls, but never one like John of God. His abandonment to God's will and his absolute confidence in God's help are almost phenomena. The heart of Our Lord is bound to be moved to aid him."

"By a miracle?"

Anthony smiled. "Peter, at this moment, any smallest donation, even a loaf of bread, would seem a miracle. I cannot say in what manner Our Lord will act through our saint, but it doesn't need a prophet to foretell that He will. Faith such as Brother Zero's does not go unrewarded." With what startling swiftness the reward was to come did not occur to Anthony Martin—nor the frightening nature of the event that was to bring it.

A few nights after the day on which Anthony and Peter concluded that a miracle alone would suffice to clear their debts, a doctor brought news that made John go pale and gape. In a flash he was gone, ripping through the dark like a meteor. Well before he reached the Royal Hospital, he heard a terrible crackling and roaring. Through rolling clouds of smoke tinged with red, he saw the hospital: a shock of flame against the night's blackness. A mob was looking on, eyes wide and blank. Not conscious of the people whom he thrust aside in his haste to reach the patients who were trapped within the burning structure, not conscious, as were the onlookers, of the gagging smoke and overwhelming heat, John dashed into the inferno.

His flame of charity outshone, outburned the consuming fire. He rushed in, rushed out, then in again, repeating these journeys of mercy for two endless hours, until, at last, he had brought several hundred patients to safety. Those who could not walk, he carried in his arms, holding their heads against his breast to protect them from the surging, suffocating smoke. At the same time, he directed the ones who were able to help themselves to follow him. Having conducted them all outside, he returned to the flaming building to fling beds, mattresses, chairs, tables, benches and linens through the windows.

Now a great, imploring cry rose up to him from the throng of fire-lit faces. "Come out! Come out! Father of the Poor, save yourself!" He did not respond. "Where is he?

There! Look!" People were screaming and pointing. "Up there! Look! He's on the roof of the south wing! John, come down! You'll be killed!"

Tranquilly, though in a voice like a roar of wind, he silenced them—and silenced the gunners who ordered him away. They had set up their cannon and intended to bombard the wing. By knocking it to pieces, they hoped to save an adjoining pavilion. Back and forth they ran, waving their arms, shouting to John to get off the roof. "Down, down, as fast as you can!"

But John remained, passive and cool as stone. Suddenly he raised his arms. The bombardiers fell silent. All that could be heard was the hissing and groaning of flames. John's voice penetrated the sounds of fire. He called down simply: "With God's help, cannon aren't necessary. Hold your fire." Then, swinging an ax which he had found, he began to break up the roof. Animated by a strength that was superhuman and seeming not to notice the flames that leapt up around him, or the red-hot heat of the roof under the soles of his bare feet, he hacked away at it for almost two hours, lifting fiercely burning rafters and throwing them to the ground. In this incredible manner, John of God saved from total destruction by bombardment the largest wing of the Royal Hospital.

A man beyond imagining!

The spectators were weak with wonder and relief. But all at once, cries went up and hands flew to faces. A long, shuddering wail went through the crowd. Suddenly enveloped by wind-twisted banners of flame, drenched in redness, looming against the night like an apparition in a garment of fire, John of God plunged through the huge gap that his ax had made.

In wordless horror and grief, Granadinos, rich and poor,

and John's two disciples, Anthony and Peter, stood mute, stricken.

And again a great cry of lamentation broke out. "Others he saved. He would not think of himself. John of God is gone. What will the poor do now?"

"Enough," said the guards, after a time. "Go to your homes."

A few of the poor looked sadly at the roofless wing that John had saved; then they turned away and left. Others would not depart, held to the spot by the curious magnetism of tragedy. Among those who would not be dismissed were Brothers Anthony and Peter. Each kept on seeing in his mind's eye the recent horrifying scene which had had about it a quality of mingled nightmare and majesty.

"Go home, Brothers," advised a man-at-arms who recognized them as John's disciples by their dark gray habits. "It's been all of a half-hour," he reminded them. "There's no help for it now, nor will there be thirty minutes hence."

But the stricken pair continued to stand where and as they were, as if the guard had not spoken. Loss and bereavement filled them. Eyes glistening with tears, faces taut, they remained side by side in a dazed silence that was broken suddenly by Anthony. "Impossible! Peter, look!" Gripping his friend's arm, he cried again, disbelievingly, "Impossible!" They sank to their knees, and then could only whisper huskily, "Jesus! Mary!"

As unexpectedly as he had fallen into the flames, John of God came walking out of them, unscathed, unscorched.

Every heart among the spectators shook with wonder and fright, and, in a voice tremulous with bewilderment, someone cried out, "Flames respect the charity of John of God!" And instantly there fell from every lip the word that caused him torment: "Saint! Saint!"

"Be not deceived, my children," John said, looking from one to the other. "You see before you John the sinner. Far from being a saint, I am nothing. I am Brother Zero." But say what he would, he could not hold down the hysterical joy of the people, or convince them that he was nothing, or prevent the outcry from going up again: "Flames respect the charity of John of God!"

To this cry there was soon to be added another: "Flood waters respect the charity of John of God!" John always gathered his firewood from the foothills of the Sierra Nevada, or fished it out of the river Genil. This river of incomparable clarity made its way from the snow-silvered Sierra Nevada through luxuriant ravines of laurel, pomegranate and myrtle, skirted the city, washed the edges of the Alameda of Granada, a tree-lined promenade, then joined the Darro in the lush Vega. After heavy rains, the Genil overflowed its banks, caused landslides, tore houses into fragments, uprooted trees and bore them along on its rapid current.

Ever concerned with the necessity to take whatever he could find for the use of his poor, John, companioned by a few Brothers, went to the river after one exceptionally heavy downpour. In the middle of the raging waters there appeared an islet which the storm had somehow formed, and on this little island a great amount of wood had collected. With never a thought to risk or danger, John swam to the heap of sand surrounded by the surging Genil. Having gathered two hundred bundles of wood, he fastened them in turn to a stout double cord and signaled to the Brothers, who then pulled the bundles to the bank. Alarmed to see a crack opening in the artificial island, they shouted to John to abandon it. As trusting as he was

daring, he called back serenely, "Keep your hearts up, Brothers. There is nothing to fear. God and His poor will protect me." Tying one last bundleful of wood to the cord, he then dove into the river. At the same moment, the island disappeared, swallowed up by the Genil.

These two miracles which the Church was to include in her decree for his canonization carried the fame of his charity far beyond Granada, and the gold that John and his Brothers needed so badly came flowing in like light to consume the shadows of their poverty. The courage of their faith was further rewarded when the Archbishop of Granada, Don Pedro de Guerrero, took John of God's hospital and growing community of Brothers under his episcopal protection.

Don Pedro was not long their protector before he realized the inadequacy of John's hospital and the restrictions it placed upon the scope of his charity, for as his
fame spread, the number of unfortunates who appealed
to him for help increased. Don Pedro's observations on
John of God's needs spurred him to summon the leading
citizens of Granada. To these he described the labors of
one man who, for some years, had endeavored to answer
entirely by himself the needs of a whole city's poor. Time
had passed. John of God had loyal followers now. Tirelessly, he and his Hospitallers gave themselves to the
service of all who came to them with their afflictions and
difficulties, and, tirelessly, John of God went through Granada's streets, to beg and to give with both hands to all
the destitute and unhappy men and women who followed
at his heels. Here was that rare man who saw and loved
Christ Crucified in his suffering fellow-men, who loved
human beings for themselves, and who gathered them to
himself by the hundreds and hundreds. The man who
called himself Brother Zero personified dedication to God
in the service of His poor. He was the right man in the right
work—but not in the right place. He required a larger
hospital.

"His present hospital cannot accommodate one quarter
of the sick poor who wish and need to be there," Don
Pedro told his listeners simply but pointedly. "It is so un-
believably crowded with the poor and the sick that it is
difficult to approach the doors, and one is hardly able to
enter the infirmaries. I appeal to your generosity in order
to assist this great servant of the poor. You cannot go amiss
by following where he leads, for his every thought and
action is directed toward God. Señores, he urgently re-

quires larger premises." Don Pedro leaned back against his chair and waited. He had not waited long when one of the grandees answered to the episcopal challenge.

"Has Your Excellence any particular place in mind?"

The Archbishop smiled. "Would it be likely that I haven't? There is an empty monastery in a good location. Needless to say, John of God hasn't the price." After a pause, Don Pedro stated the price and offered the sum of 1500 ducats from his own purse. As he knew they would, his friends pledged themselves to make up the difference. His kindly face lighted up. "Very good!" The Archbishop nodded approvingly. "Very good! I am pleased with you. Your zeal is as commendable as your generosity. You have cause to be pleased with yourselves. It is certain that you will have a share in his merits." Don Pedro steepled his fingertips, eyed them, then eyed the silk-clad grandees. "Now then, one more consideration."

"Only one?"

"More or less." Don Pedro smiled back at the questioner. "However," he said, "this is a matter which I leave for you to vote on or not, as you wish. We, as well as the poor of Granada, have John of God to thank for the relief he has given them. Not once has he appealed to the municipal administration for any kind of assistance, nor has he begged for his poor from the rich. His baskets and kettles are filled night after night by those who have not a great deal to give. It strikes me," he said to the men who were the city's administrators, "that the municipality owes it to him to lighten the burden of his expenses."

"To what extent?" asked the *alcalde primero,* who was the president of the municipal council.

"To that of paying the doctors' fees and charges for medicines. When he had but forty-six patients at a time, physicians and surgeons gave their services without charge, and apothecaries contributed the drugs for the doctors' prescriptions. John himself filled the prescriptions. After he moved from the house he first occupied to the old Carmelite monastery where he still is, and he accepted sick by the hundreds, it went against his conscience not to remunerate doctors and druggists. Some of his physicians, Sandoz and Raxis among them, refuse payment. None press him when he has nothing to pay with. Nevertheless, they justly deserve their fees and John is the first to say so."

"We agree," said the alcalde primero. "Granada can bear that expense without taking a vote, Your Excellence."

"My gratitude," said the Archbishop, "is deep. Yet it is as nothing to what his will be when I tell him the outcome of this visit. Clearly, Divine Providence is turning everything toward his wishes and needs."

Had John of God been present, he might have reminded the elated prelate that it was not in the Divine plan that he would fulfill his work for God in the time left to him with ease and without problems.

# TWENTY
# TWO

DON PEDRO'S opening pleasantries trailed off into sudden silence. He ceased his light talk to stare. Conscious of his glance, though not meeting it, John moved back a few inches in the regal chair that courtesy had forced him to take because the Archbishop offered it. Now he moved forward again to the edge of it. His bare feet echoed the shiftings of his body. Now he tucked them beneath his tunic, and now he thrust them out from under and let them sink into the velvet pile of the Oriental rug that covered the red-tiled floor.

Strange, thought the Archbishop. He is always poised and at his ease with everyone, anywhere. What does this fidgeting mean? "John, you look uncomfortable. Are you?"

Brother Zero answered with typical and winning frankness. "Yes, Your Excellence, I am."

"All because of a damask-covered chair and a rug underfoot?"

"No, Your Excellence—not that I am accustomed to damask and velvet."

"And not that I fancied you were. Far from it. I hope, though, that in your new hospital you have dropped your old habit of sleeping on the stones under the staircase."

"Thanks to Your Excellence, I have a small cell now."

"I'm glad. Have you also a bed?"

"Of a sort," John told him.

"Ha! You choose your questions carefully. Those which you feel free to answer, you reply to with artless candor. The others—" Don Pedro shook his head and smiled. "It's unlikely that you take enough sleep to merit a bed." After a short pause, he continued, "So we come back to the real reason for your discomfort—or, I should rather say disquietude. What is it?"

"Everything that isn't pleasant. Nothing new, Your Excellence. I have experienced it all before. It is nearly ten years since I began to gather up the poor. No year, no month, no week has passed without its barbs and evil rumors, without the difficulty of providing for the ever increasing numbers of the poor who come to me as their last resort. Bitter criticism is on the increase, too. I am used to it. I am prepared for it." John smiled thinly. "Brother Peter says that I am—or I was—as deaf to malicious talk as I am blind to the beauties of the city that lies all about me." As though John owed Don Pedro an apology for this, he hastened to explain, "Externals have always drifted past my vision like a streaming mist. I cannot see the marvels of Granada for the suffering in it. My ears are closed to all save cries of distress. Now—now it is different."

"Why? What makes the difference?"

"Having Your Excellence for a protector," John replied. "For myself, I do not care what people say or do. But it disturbs me to know that the rancor for which I am to blame will do Your Excellence an ill turn."

Don Pedro gave him a warm and paternal glance. "It's you," he said, "who were idealistic about mankind. I expect you still are. I know human nature too well to have illusions about it. The devil in it is everlastingly at work to persecute the good." Don Pedro paused, came to the point. "Does the ugly gossip touch especially upon your refuge for women?"

John nodded.

"What sort of things do they say?"

"Every sort, Your Excellence, except what is true and good. " 'The hungry-looking beggar,' they say of me, 'the one who goes barefoot like Saint Francis and plays hero to the poor, the same who wanders about at night, ringing a bell and telling everybody to do good to himself. *He* pours gold into a landlord's palm and buys a house with flowers and a fountain in the patio—and for no good purpose. A refuge he calls it, a safe place for lone girls and women. If they're as good as he says they are, why does he have to go there every day? If it is to be believed, they gather about him while he reads to them from the Bible and *The Imitation of Christ*. They recite the Rosary together, he makes a sermon on one of the Sorrowful Mysteries, and then he puts them to work. No dirt, no idleness. Everybody has to clean, everybody has to work. They cook, they wash, they scrub and scour and polish; they garden the patio. They sew. He himself solicits orders for them from this priest and that for altar linens and vestments. Some say that he was a shepherd once and made his own clothes out of his own homespun. Now he has the widows spinning and weaving homespun for themselves. He's turning it into a kind of convent, if that's the word.' "

Archbishop de Guerrero colored angrily. He considered these barbs and insinuations a long time and guessed rightly that John of God had repeated only the mildest. It was not hard to imagine the people who spoke in this vein of one of John's most necessary and successful charities, insulting him to his face, sneering at him and behaving with impertinence. Don Pedro's stern eyes softened as they looked at his visitor with a profound respect that he did not feel for all his fellow men.

To balance this account, John reported the help he received for his refuge from a gentleman of means and sympathy. Don Juan Fernandez contributed to the upkeep of the household and had relieved Brother Zero of the burden of scraping together marriage dowries for the girls—the detail that John insisted upon for moral reasons and for which he was earlier criticized.

Don Pedro thought: I must help him somehow, not only for his own relief but for the sake of the good that he does. That this holy man had persisted day after day and night after night for almost ten years, patiently, trustingly striving to help and save and alleviate suffering, seemed to him a continuous miracle. John of God would not lose his zeal for souls or his compassion for the unfortunate or be finished with aching for Granada's poor until he died. His charity knew no limits. That burning heart of his embraced all: the young Mary Magdalens of the streets, the widows and orphans and foundlings; the homeless, the old; paralytics, cripples, deaf and dumb mutes, the blind, the insane, incurable and lepers. Farmers in the Vega who lost their crops to bad weather, and thus their livelihood, counted on John of God to assist them until the following harvest; they could count on him as well to give them seeds and implements. To shopkeepers who had not earned sufficient income to pay their creditors for the goods they stocked, John gave the means to pay their bills and start afresh. Unemployed fathers of families, soldiers, impoverished students, individuals beset by a wrong and unable to finance a just lawsuit, sinners and penitents, apostates and embittered Moors—these, multiplied by hundreds, were John of God's crown of thorns that became as roses for him. For the sick and the poor he labored tirelessly, went hungry, went begging. Hardly had he moved his patients into his third hospital before the large donations which had come to him after the two major miracles were all used up. Unwilling to draw again upon the purses of a few generous friends, John left Brother Anthony Martin in charge of the new hospital and set out on a begging tour through the whole southern province of Andalusia. This long and fatiguing walk eventually brought him back to Granada with money enough to pay off most of his creditors and the consolation of having won to the cause of his charities several personages of wealth and rank. Among those who were to remain his loyal friends and benefactors during and after his lifetime were the Duke of Sessa and his wife, the Duchess Maria de Mendoza, and a knight who had made a name for himself during the conquest of Granada, Don Gutierro Laso de la Vega.

Don Pedro remembered well the letter that John sent off to the knight of Malaga soon after he had returned from his journey:

. . . I am in great need, the poor are so numerous . . . The patients abound . . . When donations are not sufficient I take things on credit. At this moment I owe more than 200 ducats for linen and sheets. I receive many abandoned children and look after their education. All my trust is in God, Who, I hope, will deliver me from my debts . . .

It seemed obvious to the Archbishop that God would have to deliver John from this ever increasing load, either by way of another miracle or a means that would cost John, not God, the greater effort. The fact that Brother Zero

had come to confide his problem to him was clear to the
Archbishop the moment the Father of the Poor had entered the room. There was that slow, shy smile; the reluctance he felt at having to bother anyone; the shiftings of
position that explained without words that he would rather
do anything than have to share a burden with another—
all betrayed the emotions of this giant of a saint, born to
do a giant's work, who took upon his shoulders the crosses
of all the weak and poor.

Pensively, the Archbishop stared at a neat darn in John's
tunic, and, in the same pensive silence, John of God's
sensitive fingertip followed a pattern of pomegranates
which was woven in the rose-red damask that covered the
chair arms.

*Granada will be your cross.*

Thinking aloud, John said, "I am beginning to feel it."

Don Pedro's eyes looked away from the patched place
and met his visitor's gaze. "Overwork?" he asked.

"No, Your Excellence, no. What else am I good for
except working?" He was quiet for a moment. "I held off
coming as long as I could."

"I'm here for you to come to. You're feeling the want of
money. Is that it?"

"It always is, Your Excellence. I have doubled, tripled
my begging. Yet I never have enough to meet my needs. I
am forced to buy on credit, then forced to make a loan in
order to pay my creditors, and then I must borrow from
friends if the moneylender is to get back his loan. My
critics are right. I should pay my bills before giving alms.
I know the justice of that. But the poor, the poor, there are
so many poor. I have no doubt that God will help me. He
might help me sooner if I could help myself. If only I knew
how!"

"Money you must have, a lot of it, and soon. We can't deny that." There was a little pause; then the Archbishop said, "I can think of just one way left. The Court is at Valladolid."

"The Court?" John asked, puzzled. "I can't see the connection, Your Excellency."

"The Court is the King," Don Pedro said. "Philip II is a pious man, and he isn't unfamiliar with suffering. I'm sure you would find him sympathetic to your needs."

John was more than ever astonished. "Why should he be?"

"Why should he not be? He is your King and King of all the poor you serve. Don Philip is greatly in your debt. You fought in two wars for his father, the Emperor. What you have done in less than a dozen years for hundreds, indeed thousands of his subjects, is beyond estimating. If you won't mind walking to Valladolid to see him, you can rest assured that His Majesty will put aside all else to grant you an audience. John, why do you look so baffled? Surely you don't think that Don Philip has not heard of you? Moreover, Spaniards from here to Valladolid will turn out to welcome you. Everyone of any importance will be honored to offer you hospitality."

"I don't want anyone to feel honored by my presence. All that I want is help for my poor." John's voice had dropped to a murmur.

"You will get that help if you don't turn your back on the rich. Nor should you. There are many fervent, charitable Christians among the aristocracy. Humble yourself by letting them honor you, for that will please them, though not yourself. In return, you have only to say, 'Do good to yourselves, brothers,' and they will replenish your purse over and over."

Looking unhappy about the prospect, John asked, "Does Your Excellence order me to make this journey to the King?"

Don Pedro sighed. "No, I merely encourage it as one, possibly the only, way out of your difficulties. I leave you free to decide for yourself. You wish to spare those who already have given much. What you receive from the ones who haven't an abundance to give will not suffice, and you are too humble to give the pleasure and example of your company to the rich who would open their hearts to you. To the poor you are constantly saying: 'Do good to yourselves, brothers, give alms.' Is it fair that you do not offer the same chance to prosperous Spaniards? And Philip II ought not to be an exception, either." After a silence, Don Pedro said again, "I do not order this journey. If you feel unsure about it, do what you have always done: ask the opinion of Father John of Avila."

John was lost in finger-tracing the pomegranate design again. He gave Don Pedro a swift look, then lowered his glance.

Don Pedro became increasingly uneasy. He studied the thin face that looked suddenly tired and thought to himself: His eyes always shine uncommonly. I didn't see tears in his eyes. If any man deserved to yield to a moment of weakness and discouragement, it was John of God. What he needs, Don Pedro was thinking, is a rest, not a three-hundred-and-twenty-mile walk. Getting up out of his chair, he went over and put his hands on John's shoulders, saying, "This isn't the moment to make up your mind. Don't write at once to John of Avila. You've far too much disturbing you to be other than confused. Let it go until later."

"How much later?"

"That's up to you. This is October. It will be a cold walk without shoes, hat and cloak. Give it a thought toward the end of next spring, or midsummer."

John smiled up at the Archbishop. "Next spring or summer may be too late. I am anxious, even impatient to go. Now . . . at once."

# TWENTY
# THREE

A GLACIAL wind blew off the Sierra Nevada Mountains. Brother Angelo shivered. He fixed his needle in the heap of linen that lay half on, half off, his knees, then got up to close one of the wooden shutters at the window in John of God's cell. Rubbing his hands for warmth, he stood a moment looking out. In the distance, the blackish-green spires of a row of cypress trees shivered, too. Overhead, the sky was lustrous and coldly blue as Spanish steel, the smoothness of it gashed by the white shimmer of snow peaks.

He sat down again, flexed his numb fingers and went back to darning worn places in a pile of sheets. "This is the coldest cell in the house. How does he stand it?" He spoke to Brother Dominic without looking up from his clumsy stitching. "I couldn't."

"Couldn't what?" the other asked, as he backed into the cell, carrying a very long wooden frame with a length of serge stretched upon it.

"I thought you wanted my company. I could do this darning more comfortably in my own cell. I said, how does he stand it?"

"He doesn't. He's too tall. That's not his reason for being always on his knees when he's in here, but it would be mine if I were his height."

"I didn't ask how he stands in it, merely how he stands it, the stony coldness of it. I wish he'd allow himself a brazier. Each of us has one because he says it's necessary. Yet he is the one who really needs the warmth that a few coals can throw off."

"Maybe, maybe not," said Brother Dominic. "What you need depends on who and what you are. *Fray Cero* is a saint. Look, if you're so cold, close the other shutter."

"I can't, I need the light."

Brother Dominic went over to him and glanced at the darning. He smiled indulgently and cuffed him on the jaw. "It couldn't go worse in the dark. Still, I see some improvement. When you first came, you couldn't even sew on a button. I wonder where people get the idea that sewing isn't for men? The same odd notion applies to nursing as a profession. Could any woman be gentler or more skilled at caring for the sick than Father John? As for myself, I can do things, too; that is, after Father John has taught me. You've had to rethread that needle so often, you haven't even looked up to see what I made for him. A bed. Perfect. Built to his measurements. Have a look."

Brother Angelo looked. He smiled, he frowned, he shook his head.

"Well, say something."

"As you said, Dominic, it is perfect, but if you don't take it out, he will."

"If that serge were eiderdown he would, yes."

"It'll be yes in any case. I know something about his preferences. Didn't I go to Valladolid with him?"

"Exactly why I wanted you in here while I straighten up his cell. Fray Cero has said so little about it that, if you hadn't been with him, we would wonder whether he actually went to Valladolid. A journey to see the King of Spain, and nothing to report!"

"A journey to see the poor is more like it, Dominic. If he has said little about it, that's because he is too busy, for one thing, and for another, it differed hardly at all from being at home. More walking, only that. About seven hundred miles, there and back."

Dominic looked at the bed and shrugged resignedly. "When you stayed with the rich," he asked, "did Fray Cero refuse the beds they offered? Oh, refuse is too strong a word. Fray Cero is too considerate to offend anyone in that way. I mean, did he do penance by yielding to comforts?"

"He did penance enough, but the hard way. He took great pains that no one should think him extreme or discover his habits." Angelo paused, knotted a new length of thread. "To all appearances," he went on, "he left the impression of having slept in all those carved and canopied beds. I don't know whether he fooled his hosts or not. He didn't fool me. More than one morning I found him pounding a dent in a pillow with his fist and rumpling the covers, to give the bed a slept-in look."

"*Hmm,*" said Dominic, grinning. "How did he make out at table? The nobles he stayed with must have put feasts before him."

"What feasts! I didn't know such foods existed. I'm not used to anything except bread and thin soup. He put me under obedience to eat in moderation of everything that was served."

"You didn't balk, that's obvious. Wait a moment." Brother Dominic picked up the cotlike bed and took it out of the room. "All right," he said, coming back with hot water and a scrub brush. "You dined well for the last time in your life, and what about Fray Cero?"

"Oh, a crust, a vegetable, sometimes a little fruit. Our hosts seemed to understand. None pressed him to do other than he pleased. The weather being cold, there was sure to be a log fire or an immense copper brazier full of burning coals. Not in the least self-conscious, he would take his plate, go to the hearth or to the *brasero,* spoon out ashes and sprinkle them over his food. If our hosts were surprised, they did not show it, but went right on as if it were to be expected."

Brother Dominic dipped his brush in the pail of hot suds. "We missed him," he said simply.

"He missed you, too. He was happiest when he could avoid staying with distinguished families and take lodging instead in a hospital. They were filled with sick poor. He felt at home. At times, I questioned whether we'd ever see Granada again. We never stayed in a hospital for just a night or two, but on and on. Immediately, he offered his services. I had to follow suit. It was wrong of me, I know, but we remained so long at the hospital in Toledo that I remarked to him one day that if all we were going to do was nurse the sick, we might better go home to our own."

"Was he vexed?"

"One can't vex him. No, he said to me, 'My son, we are not useless here. Our Lord affords us the occasion to practice charity toward the poor. Have a little courage and do not be impatient when there is a question of doing good.' I remembered the words but not the lesson. It was at Toledo, too, that he tried to get out of being the guest of Doña Eleanora de Mendoza, a relative of his friend, the Duchess of Sessa. The lady and her friends were wonderfully generous. When he said he would rather stay at the hospital, I told him he ought to think of her pleasure, not his own. Then he consented. In atonement for wanting his own way, he first made the Stations of the Cross for Doña Eleanora, moving from one to another of fourteen churches. His effort must have pleased Heaven because, by the time we left the house of the object of his prayers he was weighted with gold. As true as I give myself to God, as Fray Cero always says, the amount of it made my head spin!"

"Apparently it's still spinning." Dominic retrieved the spool of thread that suddenly rolled across the freshly scrubbed tiles, then picked up the pile of sheets that had slid to the floor, dumping them back into Angelo's lap. "Sew them end to end," he teased, "and you'll have a hundred yards of sheeting to wrap yourself in." A thought came to him. He snapped his fingers. "Why didn't I think of it before? You needn't have sat here shivering and shaking all this time." Crossing the cell to a small wooden coffer, he raised the lid and dragged out yards and yards of topaz velvet. "Here." He threw it over Angelo's shoulders. "It was a lady's court gown and will become either a cope or a mantle for a statue of the Blessed Virgin. Fray Cero himself ripped up all the stitches, saved every bit of thread, spread it on the floor and was meditating on it, shears in hand, when I happened to come in." Dominic smiled. "I'm positive it will adorn some image of Our Lady. There is material enough for two copes. Had he decided on a cope, he would have cut it with a sparing hand. When it's something for an image of the Holy Virgin, Fray Cero never heard of thrift. Meanwhile, she won't mind lending it to you. Warmer?"

"Much. All it needs is a hooded cowl. While the Bishop

of Tuy was about it, I wish he had given a thought to winter. Joined scapulars and a hood are what we need. Had His Lordship seen Fray Cero walking to Valladolid without a cloak, and with his head bare, in the bitter cold, I'll wager he would have added hood and scapular to his original design. Two panels of cloth put over the head so that one falls in front and the other behind haven't the warmth of a cloak, but they would be two strips more than we have."

Brother Dominic looked with fondness at the youthful Brother. "You were no warmer than Fray Cero," he reminded him.

"Frankly, I froze the whole winter. But I'm younger than he, and he forced me to wear ankle shoes. Anyhow," he smiled, "it warmed me up just to know that people recognized me as being one of his spiritual sons." Angelo bit off the thread, fingered the mended spot, and started on another worn patch. "Do you know what I think? I think the Bishop of Tuy was so magnetized by our Father that he couldn't think as far as a scapular. Had he stopped to consider that the garment symbolizes the yoke of Christ, he would surely have given it to him. Does the man live who is worthier of that symbol?"

The question required no answer. "Perhaps someday," said Dominic, "it will occur to the Bishop of Tuy or to some other." He was speaking prophetically, for, in time, the habit was to have scapular and hood, and the dark-gray color was to darken into black. "All right," said Dominic, "move your chair over there where the floor has dried. I still have this side to scrub. And whatever happened to all the gold that had your head spinning?"

"The same thing that always happens to it. We'd hardly gone beyond the city's gates when it started to pass from

Fray Cero's hands into the hands of the poor. In a twinkling, it was gone, every last piece of it. I couldn't help it,
Dominic, it made my heart sink. I said to him, 'Father,
have you forgotten why you're making this journey? Granada. Remember? Our hospital. Our needs. Our poor. Our
creditors!'"

"Did he reply?"

"He did. And in view of the crisis we were in here at
home, there is nothing I can say except that what he
replied would make sense only to a saint. He turned a
puzzled face to me and said, 'But my son, does it *matter*?
To give here or at Granada is ever to give to God. Our
Lord sends us these beggars. Can we doubt that He wishes
us to help them?' " Angelo sighed. "All the way to Valladolid that's the way it was. He received donations everywhere, promptly gave them away. To remind, chide, nag
him was no use, so I exercised heroic self-control and kept
my fears to myself."

Dominic chuckled. "And then what?"

"Well, I just let him do as he pleased. The longer I was
with him, the more I realized that a saint's logic isn't based
on the logical. His is utterly illogical, and at the same time
irresistible."

"So," said Dominic, "you arrived at a truth, you kept
your thoughts to yourself, you groaned within yourself to
see him give everything away. You must have grown in discipline." Dominic's mouth curved into a smile.

"I don't know about that, but my wits sharpened a little
under the tutelage of another Mendoza, this time the
mother of the Duchess of Sessa. A noblewoman, she is the
widow of a nobleman, Don Francisco de los Cobos. Her
home is in Valladolid. Needless to say, Fray Cero and I put
up at a pilgrims' hospital. I suspect that Doña Eleanora de

Mendoza had enlightened by letter this Doña Maria de
Mendoza, telling her the trouble she had getting Fray
Cero to be her houseguest. The great lady of Valladolid
wasted no words in pleading and argument. She knew
what to do and she knew that he couldn't rebel against it.
Ha! Fray Cero was the most astonished man in Valladolid
when he discovered that the two of us were commanded by
an order of the royal court to accept the hospitality of
Doña Maria de Mendoza for the duration of our stay. By
securing the order, Doña Maria gave him no chance for a
word of protest. He could have had anything he wanted
for the asking, but he didn't have to ask. His winning
simplicity, his piety and his magnetism drew everyone of
any consequence to his cause."

"And drew their money too, I take it. If I am right," said
Dominic with a smile, "you were hard put to it once again
to keep still."

"More than once; over and over again," declared Angelo reminiscently. "The poor swarmed around him.
That wasn't enough. He went searching them out, just
as he looks for them here. Always he was with the poor,
and always I had to bite my tongue to keep from saying,
Father, you're forgetting the king. Well, fortunately, the
Count of Tendilla, who met Frey Cero through Doña
Maria, had not forgotten the king. He arranged for the
audience. Don Philip and Fray Cero were closeted together in the royal study for several hours, at the first visit.
This in itself was thought unusual. According to the
Count, Don Philip's audiences are brief and brisk, scarcely
ever longer than ten minutes. No one seems to know what
they conversed about. Fray Cero never said anything to
me except that he found the King a kindly, easy man to
be with, which isn't the impression Don Philip usually

gives. Most people, papal nuncios among them, appear to be afraid of him. Later, I heard through the Count of Tendilla that, when Fray Cero went before the King, he said, with his characteristic simplicity: 'My Lord, I am accustomed to call all men Brother. You, who are my prince, by what name should I call you?' The King told him to call him by any name he pleased. Sometimes habit overruled and he addressed the King as Brother; at other times, he called him 'Good Prince.' After the first visit, he had little chance to elude the King. His Majesty's sisters, the Infantas, asked to meet him, and then their friends. I know nothing of those meetings except that Don Philip, the Princesses and the friends of the royal family were immensely generous. One lady of the court said she had no money to give him and dropped into his hands instead a fabulously valuable necklace of pearls, diamonds and rubies. When he thanked her he said: 'Such is the power of charity. It takes from the rich their superfluous ornaments to cover the suffering members of Jesus Christ.' He sold it without delay and received a great amount for it."

"The royal donations, the jewels," said Dominic, "it all went into food and clothing for the poor of Valladolid?"

"All of it. And he alone knows how many indebtednesses he paid for the poor."

Dominic shook his head as if in wonder. Then he asked, "Where did your sharpened wits come in?"

"At the end. Fray Cero was getting restless. He wanted to come home. I don't think he gave a thought to the fact that he'd leave Valladolid as empty handed as he had left Granada. He just wanted to come home to his own. Everybody knew that the donations he had received had been spent on the poor of Valladolid. Doña Maria, may God bless her and Our Lady embrace her, gathered her rich and influential friends together once more. They agreed that they couldn't let him go home with nothing more than love and comfort for the poor of Granada. That's when I stepped in. I had to, Dominic. I found an opportunity to speak in private with Doña Maria. It wasn't necessary to explain or defend my worry. She saw eye to eye with me in this matter. 'If you and your friends give him money,' I said to her, 'he'll enrich every pauper with it before we are beyond sight of Valladolid.' I suggested that, instead of money, they give him letters of credit and make them payable nowhere but in Granada. I hated to conspire against his marvelous charity, but he left me no choice. One of us had to remember the reason for the journey, had to consider the day when the Archbishop would have to be faced, and—" Angelo sighed—"the one of us who is not a saint had to use ordinary logic."

"Don't be disturbed, Angelo. You're not guilty of betrayal or cunning. You did the right thing. Were you to tell him about the letters of credit when he's in a practical frame of mind, he'd be the first to thank God for giving you the inspiration. Who can doubt that he hasn't his feet on the ground most of the time? Less than ten years in a man's life is nothing. Yet see what he has achieved in that short space of time! An enormous, incredible amount of work, and the largest part of it he undertook and accomplished alone. He didn't get it done by being dreamy and impractical. I say again, don't worry about your recommendation to Doña Maria de Mendoza. There was virtue in it and happiness for Fray Cero. Only think what consolation it is for him to be able to pay his bills. Not to owe anyone anything! And maybe to have a bit left over, even. That would be a new experience for him."

"It would be a novelty for all of us," said Angelo. "But

it won't be. This morning, when I left him, he was running up a bill the total of which I'd rather not imagine."

"Oh, no!"

"Oh, yes!"

"You ought not to have left him." There was mild reproach in Dominic's tone.

"I'd nothing to say about it. In his quiet way, he ordered me home, told me to mend the sheets that I would find in his cell, or to pluck the pinfeathers from the chickens the Marquis of Tarifa sent. I decided in favor of darning sheets."

"Where did you leave him?"

"In a shop. It's part tailor shop, part haberdashery. The tailor-haberdasher is a woman."

"What on earth was he doing there?"

"Being recklessly extravagant. Oh, but Dominic, he was so happy, and the children were delirious with delight. You see," Angelo explained, "as we walked away from a cheese shop where Fray Cero settled his account, we came upon a band of little urchins. There must have been ten or twelve. Of course, they knew him. They jumped around him like crickets, shouting, '*Padrecito! Padre de los Pobres!*—Little Father! Father of the Poor!' They begged a sweet. Neither of us had a piece of candy to give them. Fray Cero looked on the verge of tears. But it wasn't for lack of candy. It was their lack of clothing. They were in rags, all of them shivering, lips blue with cold, their teeth chattering. He stooped, opened his arms and gathered the lot of them to him. A look of sheer delight shone in his eyes as he kissed and caressed them. He has a true Spanish love for children. I'm not sure how many he carried, but more than I could have done. I managed with one on each arm. That was my limit. The bigger ones hopped along beside him, clinging

to his habit. Presently, we were in this shop which appeared
to cater especially to children. Fray Cero obviously was a
regular customer. The woman was overjoyed at seeing him.
He spoke to her in whispers. She replied in a hearty voice.
Yes, yes, by all means. Gladly would she extend credit."
Angelo glanced up to see if there was any anxiety on
Dominic's face. There was only a smile, and a strange look,
almost too sad. Then he brightened. "So," he said, "Fray
Cero fitted them out from head to foot, eh?"

"All the way. He let them have anything they wanted.
Blissfully unaware of the value of money, they chose shirts,
breeches, doublets, little capes, velvet berets with plumes

drooping on them and slippers with shining buckles. The finest wool, the softest velvet. You never heard such squealing in your life! As for Fray Cero, he was in heaven. When all the garments for each child had been assembled, he knelt on the floor, drew the smallest boy to him and proceeded to dress him. He wouldn't let the woman help; he quite forgot about me, oh, for quite a while. This was the first time that I heard him laugh enough for me to catch the beauty of his laughter. He laughed, he hummed, he stroked their heads, took their faces between his hands and kissed them. When he finally remembered me, he turned, smiled and flushed, as though he felt guilt at being so happy. I offered to dress some of the children. He said, 'Please, Angelo, let me do it. I have a reason.' Then he told me to go home and busy myself. I pondered the reason all the way home. It wasn't until I made a visit to the chapel and looked at Our Lady with the Holy Child that it came to me. The apparition at Guadalupe."

A silence fell between them.

"Angelo, I'm afraid," Brother Dominic said suddenly.

"Why are you afraid? Of what?"

"I can't say exactly. Just a feeling that comes over me, more and more often. One day I look at him and I say to myself: his strength is immortal. The next I wonder how he has ever managed to live as long as he has. He will be fifty-five next March, if he lives to see another birthday. He won't rest; he won't look after himself. He works incessantly. It costs us an effort to be cheerful in the continual presence of pain and misery and death. What must it cost him? His sensitiveness is greater than ours. He is burdened with a thousand cares. Not the least of them are the slanders and lies that are spread about Granada day after day. He feels them intensely. In the presence of others, he never gives himself away. But my cell is next to his. I know what he goes through. Many's the night I've heard him sobbing and praying for his attackers. Physically and emotionally, he is wearing himself out in the service of others—for love of God—and God seems to exact more rather than less of him." Dominic paused.

The chill in the cell seemed to become more pronounced. The needle shook in Angelo's stiff fingers. He wrapped the amber velvet court gown more tightly about him. The silence between the two men had a quality that each felt but could not have described. And how the thought of their spiritual father filled it! A blast of wind sent the sheets whirling the length of the cell. Neither man appeared to care.

"Dressing those children—" Dominic began, and could not go on.

"I wish you had been there. His happiness was complete."

"Angelo, he dressed the Infant Jesus in the church at Guadalupe. He understood the apparition to mean that he was to clothe, feed and care for the needy. Having clothed those street children, it's—" Dominic's strong voice faltered—"it's as though he had come full circle."

"Full circle?" echoed Angelo. "You mean—?" And then, with urgent and pleading inquiry: "Do you mean that you see some link between the two . . . that having come full circle, he has come to the end?"

There wasn't any answer.

# TWENTY
# FOUR

Too wasted with work and fasting to resist, the burdened Brother Zero, who rarely was sick, came down with a heavy cold shortly before Christmas. A day or two on his fiber mat in the quiet of his cell, and he was up again. Fear of infecting the patients kept him out of the wards, and he assigned to another his own hours in the kitchen. But he swept, scrubbed and polished the corridors, the patio and the vestibule; he laundered and ironed clothing and linens. Afternoons, he disappeared from his hospital with provisions and alms for the families that depended on his daily help.

His afternoon visits made, John dragged himself home, only to go forth again when the day's light had faded away and the snow crowns on the Sierra peaks no longer glittered in the sunset like diadems of many-colored jewels. In the darkening night, Granada heard the ringing of his bell and the pleading voice: *Do good to yourselves, brothers.*
. . . Bell and cry would come to an abrupt stop. Exhausted himself, John would hurry up or down a street to give a helping hand to some sick poor who had collapsed. Frail and weakened, there was not much left of him except compassion. Yet this pure flame of charity was still sufficient to enable him to carry an inert body over each shoulder, or a

man far heavier than himself in his arms.

Then, after a few nights of this kind of effort, nature rebelled and John was forced to yield to fatigue. By Christmas Eve, he looked and felt more like himself. He went to the kitchen to fetch his hamper, pots and bell, but collected three axes instead and summoned two Brothers, Cristobal and Rodrigo.

"Father, you're not going out in this cold! You mustn't."

"I am and I must, and you are going with me," he said, and gave an ax to each.

"Yes, Father." Cristobal stared down at the ax in his hand. "But why this?" he asked.

"Cristobal, do you hear anything in here?"

The Brother listened, shook his head. "Nothing, Father."

"Nothing is right." John smiled. "Not even a twig is crackling. The broth in that cauldron won't cook without heat. We haven't a stick of wood. Come along, Brothers."

The three made for a forest where John habitually went for wood. It was dark and cold, bitterly cold, with a sharp wind moaning in the pines. Twigs crunched under their feet, but branches, let alone tree trunks, made no sound under the blows of the axes.

"The wood is too wet, Father. It won't give." Rodrigo looked over his shoulder, evidently expecting to find drier wood. Eyes staring, mouth wide open, he stood as though turned into stone. Then he reached gropingly for Cristobal.

"What is it? What are you looking at?" Cristobal's eyes followed the other's pointing finger. Startled, Cristobal gasped, drew his hand across his eyes, then looked once again. They were, he thought, in a world of towering trees and towering men without reality, for out of the blackness two woodcutters of immense height and build had appeared, noiselessly. Without a word, they felled half a dozen trees, cut the branches, cut logs and bundled faggots in such quantities and with such speed as to leave the two Brothers incapable of thought. Incredulous, they looked on, then turned inquiring glances on John, who said nothing seeming to accept it as perfectly natural that a pair of giant woodsmen should assist them.

"Father," whispered Cristobal, "who are they? Did you send for them to help us?"

John stood straight and tall in the unlit darkness. He, too, seemed outside the world of reality. He made no reply.

Keeping his voice very low, Rodrigo asked, "Where on earth could they have come from?" Fear prickled through him for a second, as the thought occurred to him that they might not be of this earth. He looked at the enormous amount of wood. At least the wood was real. "Ay! it will take us how many trips to this forest to haul all that wood to the hospital!" He addressed no one in particular. In front of him the gloom seemed thicker, and through it came a voice. "Do not worry, Brother. We have cut the wood and we shall help you carry it off."

It was a very calm John of God, and two shaky and bewildered Brothers, who finally left the forest, each one bearing as much wood as his arms would hold. Unnerving enough, for the Brothers, to have seen and heard mystery without the added worry of feeling rather than seeing their way through impenetrable blackness. One misstep could plunge any one of them into a deep ravine.

John led the way, sensing the nervousness of the two behind. He could hear their quick, uneven breathing. Now and again they stumbled on a rock or a branch and caught themselves just in time. His stride was longer than theirs.

He shortened it, as he felt them hurry a little to come nearer to him. It was thoughtless of him, he was thinking, to have brought them along, for at night the forest was dark as an open grave. They weren't familiar with the trails. He was. At that, he could not see his hand before his face, much less the ground. His own footing became uncertain. And even as he realized this, he looked up suddenly, his eyes drawn by a red glow. Just above him, two strong, straight-burning torch flames blazoned the darkness. Now before their feet the narrow, tortuous path became brighter than in daylight. The hands that held the torches remained hidden, invisible. The flames guided the three men until they reached their hospital, then became smaller and smaller and vanished upward on the wind, like two blown sparks.

"Where did they come from? Where did they go? I don't understand it," said Cristobal, little dreaming that yet another wonder was to take his breath away.

Passing from the vestibule into the patio, the three stopped short.

"It can't be!" gasped Rodrigo. "And yet—"

Yes, and yet there it was—all the wood which they had believed would have them going to and from the forest every day for a week, the piles of it were so enormous.

"Mysteries, so many mysteries in one night!" exclaimed Rodrigo in a shaken voice. "Why?"

John said, very quietly, "These marvels were not performed for us but for our poor, who are dear to God. He attends them in His own way, for He sees what a weak servant they have in me. A miserably weak servant," he said tiredly and leaned against a stack of wood to steady himself. Once again he was exhausted to the point of numbness. "Go to the wards," he said to the Brothers, "and tell our poor to praise and adore Our Lord and Savior Whose birth we commemorate this night. It is on their account that the Light of the World deigned to illuminate our way and bring us safely home."

The two Brothers looked at him for a little in silence, and then they did his bidding.

Alone, John of God gazed up at the sky. The moon came from behind the silvery vapor of a cloud, and over all the heavens a myriad of stars were strewn. Quiet. So quiet. But precisely at midnight the silence would be shattered by the clang and pound and peal of church bells. How well he knew them all! He could hear them without their being rung. For a long moment there was nothing else in his ears. Then through the clamor of sound his own voice came, telling him that never again would he see the stars and hear the bells of Christmas.

# TWENTY
# FIVE

DR. RAXIS was in a mild frenzy. "Now,
understand," he said to Brother Anthony, "I am not
blaming you for anything, but how in the name of Heaven
could you let him go to the river for wood after that spring
flood we had?"

"No one let him. He simply went without our knowing."

"Why wasn't a Brother in constant attendance?"

"He won't have one. He won't be put to bed in the
infirmary. He won't lie anywhere but on the floor of his
cell. That he stayed there for a week is a wonder. Urge
any least comfort on him and he becomes so distressed that
one has to give in to him." Brother Anthony showed his
own distress by pacing back and forth in the small room
which he used as an office.

"If he's to live," warned the doctor, "you'll have to stop
giving in to him."

Anthony came to a standstill. "Doctor, we aren't dealing
with an ordinary man. John of God is a single-hearted
servant of the Cross. The Divine Passion speaks in him; he
relives it every day. It is his way to God. Compassion, sacrifice, prayers, prayers, sacrifice, compassion. His whole life
has been an act of charity and an act of penitence. Are we
to forbid his penances now? Do you think it is easy for us

275

to lavish care on everyone except our spiritual Father? It isn't. Yet when he entreats us to leave him his cross, we know that by begging him to accept one comfort or another we only sadden him, and he has grief enough. The drowning of the youth who went to the river with Father John and Brother James preys on his mind. It is a constant anguish to him. You see, Doctor, he honestly believes that his own sins were the cause of the tragedy. No calamity occurs but he lays it to his sins. Now he feels that what he calls his sinfulness threatens us all."

"But, Anthony, that's absurd!"

"Not to a saint's way of thinking. Many great penitents were tormented by the same obsession, Catherine of Siena and Margaret of Cortona among them. Catherine attributed heresies and schisms to her sins. Margaret regarded all human misery as a direct effect of her wrong-doing. We average Christians leave the confessional with a certain peace of mind. Our sins are blown out by absolution the way candle flames are snuffed. We see them no longer and seldom look back on them. Pardon consoles us. The penitential saint is not consoled as we are. Though they be no bigger than a grain of sand, the sins of his past continue to haunt him. They are ghosts that will not be laid, and all the penances the saint performs cannot drive them away. His solitary consolation lies in penance."

"Anthony, I appreciate your point of view. Nevertheless, I am a physician. I have my duties toward John, too. He has to be persuaded that the death of that boy was an accident. Our good Father of the Poor has an extraordinary understanding of the human heart. As soon as he admits a patient and puts him to bed, he calls the priest. He knows better than most that a sick spirit is no help to a sick body. *Why* can't he apply the same wisdom to himself? And what's the matter with Father Portillo? He's his confessor."

Brother Anthony smiled faintly. "Father Portillo has talked to him for hours, to no purpose. If I believed it would help, I'd send for Father John of Avila. It wouldn't help, though. They're two of a kind. Over and over, Brother James, who witnessed it, has gone to him and said: 'Adriano went too far into the river. The water was flowing like a gale of wind. You shouted to him to come back. He couldn't hear you above the roar. Then you braved that turbulent river and swam toward him. He was almost within your grasp, but the current was treacherous. It dragged him under and away. You did everything you could to save him, Father, while I stood by, petrified, fearing for both your lives. When you get well, you must teach me to swim.' "

"John says nothing? Just turns his face to the wall?"

"He cries out for mercy and forgiveness," said Anthony. "That is all."

"Was Adriano a former patient?"

"No, Doctor. He came here asking for kitchen work. He was a good youth, quick at his chores and devoted to our Father."

"I can understand, then," said the Doctor, "why Adriano went with John without raising a question, but I find it odd that Brother James, who surely knew that he'd been very ill, did nothing to prevent him from going to the Genil. At the very least, he ought to have informed you."

With some of John's own charity, Brother Anthony said, "It isn't odd, really. He has been here only a few weeks. He wasn't aware of how sick our Father had been, and when he was approached by him, he thought him fully recovered. Like the rest of us, James was delighted to do his bidding. That morning, you may remember, Father

John seemed entirely well. He was all over the hospital, giving off energy like sparks."

"I remember," said the doctor gloomily. "I told him to stop showing off and go back to his cell where he belonged. Wasted words, of course. He merely smiled at me." Dr. Raxis straightened his back and sighed. "Had he not thrown himself into that icy river, had he not gone out the very next morning, against my orders, he'd not be in the shape he's in now. It's serious, Anthony."

"I know. I took his pulse count an hour ago. When we're with him, he pretends he has no pain, no difficulty in breathing. Yet every breath he takes is a stab in his chest. His eyes are glazed with fever. He looks at you vaguely, closes his eyes. Sometimes he murmurs incoherently, always something about bills and payments due. Our poor Father!" Anthony returned to the chair at his table. "No use telling ourselves that everything is all right, and even less use saying that to him. He knows better than we how sick he is. He knew it the morning after the day he went to the Genil for wood."

"Then, by all the Saints," said the doctor excitedly, "why didn't he stay at home?"

"Because, Doctor, his sense of responsibility to others outweighs any consideration for himself."

"Is there any reason why one of you couldn't have done his begging and distributing for him that day?"

"None. As far as that goes, Brother Piola went in his stead. See these?" Anthony showed the Doctor three large ledgers. "When John came to me that morning and asked me to accompany him, he had one of these account books in his hand. I didn't know the reason, and I tried to make him postpone the errand. He was trembling, partly from weakness and shock, partly from what seemed to me to be alarm. There was an impatience about him, that of a man who has much to do and little time left. But never have I seen him steadier of purpose. There was no putting him off or forcing him back to his straw mat. I knew that, if I didn't go with him, he would go alone, so I went."

"And what was it all about?" asked the doctor.

"The usual thing. Goods bought on credit, money owing. Together we went to every merchant from whom we buy supplies of one kind and another. His fingers shook as with palsy, yet he wrote down their names, the items obtained from them and the sum of our indebtedness to each. This extended errand consumed most of the day. He used what remained of it, as well as the night, on the other two ledgers. In this one he listed our furniture, utensils, dishes, linens and instruments, which means that first he had to go from ward to ward and cell to cell, from closet to cupboard, and take account of everything in the hospital."

Dr. Raxis was more than ever amazed at the zeal and high sense of duty that had driven a gravely sick man to do what any doctor not only would have forbidden but would have believed to be beyond human strength. "And what is in the third ledger?"

"The hospital regulations, most precisely put, as well as the general routine to be followed by the Brothers and the volunteers respectively. To the individual Brother he has assigned specific duties to be performed at given hours of the day and night. In short, Doctor, he hasn't overlooked or neglected a single thing."

For a long, silent moment, Anthony and the doctor gazed at the three big ledgers. Their unspoken thoughts probably were similar. Dr. Raxis pondered the painstaking care and integrity that every page represented. In order to spare his Hospitallers confusion and bother, John characteristically had not spared himself. That he was ill and sorrowful enough to have been excused from doing anything would not have entered his mind. The physical effort, the time and patience, the damage to his health, if it could be said that he had health, and the emotional strain that it must have cost him, filled Peter Raxis with reverent respect. He knew John too well not to realize the heartache that had gone into this purely practical task. Last acts are last acts, and, while a saint may long for death because it means the ultimate in union with God, he nevertheless is human. The intensely affectionate nature of John of God made him especially lovable and human.

Dr. Raxis drew up his chair closer to the table. "If you've no objections, Anthony, may I have a look at the book of regulations?"

"Certainly." Anthony gave it to him, saw him leaf through the pages, then return to the introduction which John had written. It became plainer by the minute that Dr. Raxis was astonished, and with his astonishment came a profound admiration as well as puzzlement. Without putting the ledger down, he asked Anthony, "Where was he schooled?"

"Nowhere that I know of, except at the side of the parish priest in Oropesa. He never fails to pray for that priest because he taught him to read and write."

"He taught him well," murmured the Doctor, turning a page. "I had no idea of this fund of knowledge. He's obviously an avid reader. But where," he asked, looking at Anthony, "are the books?"

"Books?"

"Haven't you read this preamble or whatever it is? I'd call it a summation of his opinions and sympathies."

"Oh that, yes, I read it. I don't recall any mention of books."

"He doesn't name or quote from them. But it is evident that he knows the theories of reputable medical men of the past and present."

"He used to haunt a bookshop in Gibraltar," Anthony remembered. "He himself peddled religious books. The others he may have read in the shop, and it's possible that he has borrowed books from doctors."

"Well, wherever he got them, he skipped no single word. The theories and findings of Laguna, Arceo, Lobera, Vesalius, the late Swiss physician Paracelsus, are all here, together with his own deductions." Peter Raxis reread a passage and smiled. "As I would expect, the men whose views he agrees with are thinkers and fearless individualists. They have all taken leave of Galen's doctrines and have suffered opposition as a consequence. I wonder if John ever came across the work of Henri de Mondeville? French. Thirteenth–fourteenth century. A brilliant man who went his own way, and it wasn't the way of the ancient Greek physician, Galen. Mondeville upset the whole medical profession of his day by saying, 'God did not exhaust all His creative power in making Galen.' Mondeville often wrote and spoke with tongue in cheek. I particularly like his prescription for keeping the patient cheerful. 'Keep up your patient's spirits,' he wrote, 'by music of viols and ten-stringed psaltery. Or by forged letters describing the death of his enemies, or by telling him that he has been elected to a bishopric, if he is a churchman . . . Never dine with a patient who is in your debt, but get your dinner at an inn, otherwise he will deduct his hospitality from your fee.' Mondeville struck hard blows at superstition and traditional concepts and earned the hostility of his colleagues. The man who doesn't conform must pay the price. Take Vesalius, the young Belgian physician. He studied at Padua. Seven years ago, his great work on anatomy was published. In it, he threw aside Galen's teachings, denounced the superstitions of the ancients and described body structures until then unknown. Result: he was shouted out of Padua as a heretic. We are fortunate to have him in Spain. He came here at the invitation of Emperor Charles and Don Philip and serves as their personal physician. He certainly would not have gone to England. Although he has been in his tomb these three years, the law that Henry VIII decreed against thinkers remains in effect. He called it: *An Act for Abolishing Diversity of Opinion*. As for Doctor Paracelsus, he was maligned not only for his medical beliefs but for the people he helped and associated with. Accused of disgracing his profession because he held among his friends persons who were considered to be beneath his level, he made a reply that John of God might have given. 'A gem is a gem,' he said, 'whether found in a jewel box or in a garbage heap.' "

Looking again at John's written thoughts, he spoke as if speaking to himself: "Obvious, too, is the influence of the *Thesaurus Pauperum*. I can see why the *Treasury of The Poor,* by the physician-Pope, John XXI, would appeal to John of God. It embodies all the pity and charity that he exemplifies in his life and work. Again a man who did his own thinking, it is possible that before he became Pope, Peter Hispanus was slandered, too."

Dr. Raxis stood up, placed the ledger on the table. "When I have more time, I should like to read it all. I expect he has entrusted these ledgers to you."

Anthony's suddenly husky voice answered him. "Yes, he entrusted them to me in the presence of the Brothers and had me read the contents aloud to them. To each page he affixed his signature: *Y F O—Yo Fray Cero* (I Brother Zero).

"What it amounts to, Anthony, is that he has made you his successor."

"Rather say that I am replacing him during his illness. God can cure him all in an instant, if that is His will. We are praying that it is."

"It will be something of a miracle," said Dr. Raxis, "if I find him lying quietly on his bed. And what a bed! Two boards on the floor, with a fiber mat over them."

"You can be sure of that 'miracle.' He is too weak today to want to move. Since he doesn't want anyone with him, I've stationed Brother Dominic outside his door. Dominic's ears are attuned to his every breath."

"Good! I'll go to him now. I'll do my best, Anthony."

"Yes, I know you will." Anthony leaned his elbows on the table and covered his face with his hands. When he dropped his hands and looked up, Dr. Raxis was gone.

It was not long before he was back. Anthony sprang to his feet. "No, Anthony, it isn't what you think. But it's bad enough. You said he was too weak to move. He not only moved, he got up, dressed, thrust Dominic out of his way and left the house."

"What!" Anthony stared at him with a kind of terror. "You aren't serious, Doctor. He can't have gone out."

"I was never more serious."

"Where has he gone?"

"To the archepiscopal palace. Dominic pleaded, tried to reason with him, tried to hold him back. They both were absent when I got to his cell. Dominic had followed him. Peter Velasco came after me to explain."

"Explain what? Does he know why he went to the Archbishop so suddenly?"

"He told me that Don Pedro sent a message saying that he wished to see John as soon as possible." Doctor Raxis regarded him somberly. "Did no one tell His Excellency that John was ill?"

"No, Doctor, we didn't. He'll know it when he sees him. Who took the message?"

"A Brother, an outside helper, I'm not sure which. Whoever it was gave it to Dominic, who gave it to John." Dr. Raxis stared wretchedly at the ledgers. "Anthony, he has a severe inflammation of the lungs. He was sick when he went to the Genil for wood, he is sicker now. What are we to do with him? What *can* we do?"

"Until he returns, nothing. I can't think that the Archbishop won't send him straight home. I can't think, either, what would be so urgent as to require His Excellency to summon him."

# TWENTY
# SIX

D R. RAXIS said he'd be only a few minutes." Brother Anthony's eyes fixed themselves on the door of John's cell with growing anxiety. "It's a long time, isn't it?" Anthony spoke in tones as hushed as the cloister corridor, where all was quiet and dim as twilight. "Oh, Dominic, if only you had brought him home immediately! Why did you let him stay?"

"You know better than to ask that. His spirit is stronger than his body, stronger than mine. My best wasn't enough, but I tried my best to stop him in the first place. Who can? He firmly pushed me out of his way and said, 'If I lose my health, to what better cause can I lose it than obedience? His Excellency has summoned me. I must go.' I ran after him, pleaded again, to no avail. Later, Don Pedro told me that the instant he saw Fray Cero he knew he was ill. He urged him to go home. Fray Cero insisted he was quite well enough to listen to whatever it was that Don Pedro wished to say to him. Worse yet, as if to prove it, he knelt the whole time, even though His Excellency repeatedly asked him to take a chair." Brother Dominic paused, fingered the rosary that hung from his cincture. "It would be hard to say whether His Excellency was more distressed by Fray Cero's determination to stay or by the

*285*

disagreeable matter that had to be aired."

Instantly, Anthony's thoughts flew to the heaped ledgers. Anger quickened in him as he jumped to the conclusion that John's creditors had lodged complaints against him with the Archbishop.

"They may hound but they don't malign Fray Cero," Dominic said and cast a meaningful look at the other.

"Slanderers again?"

"Yes."

"Strange," said Anthony, "that's what Dr. Raxis was talking about. The slander and abuse that are suffered by great and isolated men of science, for no better reason than that they accomplish good for humanity. Well, what are the faultfinders crying about now?"

"The usual. Fray Cero supports the undeserving; helps those who ought to be made to help themselves; encourages idleness by giving alms; he doesn't ask questions, doesn't inquire into the past of the women and girls to whom he has given refuge; his night-shelter is a den of thieves; his hospital is a haven for hardened sinners, *et cetera.* Don Pedro quieted the accusers with difficulty and found himself compelled to promise that he would investigate their charges." Dominic waited a moment. "It isn't in Fray Cero to appease the exaggerated pride of snobs. Humility is the essence of him. Merely as a matter of principle, Don Pedro had to question him."

"I hope he wasn't too ill to defend himself."

"He defended his work, not himself. All his strength was used up by the time he reached the Archbishop's palace, but his zeal and humbleness are inexhaustible. 'If I received only the good,' he told Don Pedro, 'our wards would be empty and I would have no sinners to convert. I know that I do not perform my duty as I ought. I have set a bad example. I am unworthy of the trust that has been given me, an unworthy guardian of my Brothers. Were you to visit our hospital you would not find the abuses and evil persons that Your Excellency has been warned are in it, and you would realize at once that I am the only one who ought to be driven out.' " Dominic was twisting his beads in his restless hands. "If His Excellency had not taken me aside for a moment," he explained to Anthony, "I wouldn't have known what the summons was all about, although I suppose I might have guessed it by something that Fray Cero said to me when we came home. As we entered the vestibule, he put his hand on my shoulder and looked at me. His eyes seemed to beg forgiveness. I didn't know for what until after he had spoken. The counsel that he gave I am sure he was giving to every one of us. This is what he said: 'We are human, subject to error and mis-understandings, and quick to judge. So let us pardon, yes, let us pardon as we wish to be pardoned. Judgment is God's alone. Let us serve God faithfully, for it is to Him and to His Blessed Mother that we are answerable.' "

There was silence.

All at once, Dominic's forced calm deserted him. His eyes swam. Biting down on his lip, he stared at the door which led to John's cell. He wanted to go to it, thrust it open and throw himself on his knees before the beloved Fray Cero. What was Dr. Raxis saying to their Father? What thoughts was the Doctor keeping to himself? Dominic looked away from the door and gazed down at the floor. Everything reminded him of Brother Zero: the polished garnet-colored tiles, the polished wood of the gallery rail-ing and its bars of carved cedar; the lime-whitened walls, always spotlessly white. The stark whiteness of the two end walls was relieved by paintings which were given by friends. The one was a large gold-framed canvas of the Blessed Virgin in a seated position, dressed in a rose-red gown stippled all over with little flowers which the Holy Child investigated with a delicate finger, as He stood on her knee. The other was an ashen, blood-dripping Christ on the gibbet between the blue-mantled Virgin and Saint John's emerald cloak flecked with gold leaf. Under each painting was a semi-circular shelf holding a pottery bowl of pink and scarlet clove-pinks, as though to perfume the painted flowers on the Virgin's gown and to soften with fragrance the suffering of Jesus, His Mother and Saint John.

Both Brothers suddenly were jarred out of their reflections by two sounds that came to them simultaneously. They heard Doña Ana Osorio greeting a Brother in the patio which was just below the second-floor gallery. Friend and benefactress, Doña Ana had been several times to visit the ailing saint and had not minced words about his needing absolute quiet and every possible care. Just now, however, more important to Anthony and Dominic than the arrival of the wealthy widow was the appearance of Dr. Raxis.

He closed the door quietly behind him and came toward the two. He said what had to be said. They listened to him as to a distant voice.

"There's nothing to be done for him, nothing at all?" Anthony was dazed and unwilling to accept that John of God stood little if any chance to recover. "There must be something, there has to be. We need him."

"He is extremely ill," said Dr. Raxis with more calm than he felt. "There isn't much to be done for him now." He heard the faint moan that escaped Anthony's lips and gripped the Brother's shoulder. "There is something," he said, "that John would want you to do for yourselves: grieve less and pray more." The doctor regarded them with sympathy. Then, still very calmly, he continued, "Do exactly as he wishes. If he wants to be alone, let him be alone; if he wants to see his friends, admit them for a few minutes."

Dominic cleared his throat, asked hoarsely, "About how long has he?"

"I don't know. John knows. I suspected that he knew. He evaded a direct answer, but he told me that he is sure it will happen on a Friday or a Saturday. This week or next or the next after?" Dr. Raxis shook his head. "That is John's secret. There is no fear in him, no regret. He is all tranquility and joy. The greatest service that you can do him is to rejoice with him. It is as simple as that. And as hard." He tried to smile. "I'll come in again tonight," he said, and left them standing in a stunned and brooding silence that suddenly was interrupted by the light yet purposeful step of Doña Ana Osorio.

She was dressed in crisp black silk. A rosary spilled crystal from her belt, and from her broad-brimmed, halolike hat hung a drift of black lace that flowed down her back. The two Brothers saw only a piece of parchment which was folded and sealed with red wax. She held it in her hand and it flared against the blackness of her wide skirt. They could not take their eyes off it, and they wondered what it meant.

After a moment, Brother Anthony tapped softly on John's door, went in, asked if he would see Doña Ana for a minute, then opened the door and invited her in. She had no intention of wearying John with conversation she assured Brother Anthony, and asked him to remain in the room, for she expected she would require his help. Doña

Ana felt a pang of sadness as she looked at John's face. Penance and pain seemed to have chiseled it down to the bone. Without speaking, she gave him the parchment. He glanced at the seal, recognized the crest stamped upon the wax as that of Don Pedro de Guerrero. Quickly he broke it, opened the page and read the single sentence written on it in the stately handscript of the Archbishop. This sentence was the final nail that was to fix John of God to his cross.

John lifted his head from the little alms basket that he used for a pillow and looked at her. He was dazed and incredulous. "Señora, what have you done?"

"My duty," she said softly.

"But what of mine?"

"It is written there. His Excellency commands you in the name of Obedience to obey me as you would obey himself."

John lay back on his bed of boards and closed his eyes. "Why, señora, why?"

"Because you must let yourself be cared for."

"If this sickness is to end in my death, what better place can I wish to die in than this? And if my health is to be restored, where shall I regain it more quickly than here?"

"That might be the case, Father John, if you did not let your heart rule your mind."

Opening his eyes, John looked at Anthony. The look said that to sever himself from his poor and his Brothers would be as painful as to tear his heart apart. Slowly, Anthony came to his side. He murmured, "Doña Ana is right." Anthony smiled at him. "All her concern is for your well-being. His Excellency shares her solicitude for you." He paused, sensed the rising misery and confusion in John and wondered how long his own forced courage would

last. Then, with quiet good humor, he said, "Doña Maria de Mendoza had the wit to secure a royal court order as the one way to press hospitality upon you. Now again it is a woman's foresight that may restore you to health. Being men, it never entered our heads to appeal to Don Pedro as a last resort. Yet how well we know that you cannot be made to rest or be properly attended except by written command! And surely His Excellency commands you under the guidance of Our Lord. Don Pedro isn't sending you to the stake but to a devout and well-ordered household where you will be released from distractions and worries, and from the sight and sounds of sufferings which only increase your own."

For a moment Anthony thought that John had not heard. But then he gazed up at the Brother, his eyes sad

and imploring. Anthony remained still. Pity for the Father
of the Poor crushed his heart. That John was struggling
with his thoughts was plain enough. The conflict showed
in his anguished expression. Then, gradually, the look of
pleading left his face, and resignation marked his features.
He was like a man recovering after a strenuous exertion.

He said, at last, very firmly, "The Son of God obeyed
His Father unto death, even unto death on the cross. His
most unworthy servant, John, shall to the last moment of
his life adore and honor that obedience." There was a
silence that seemed filled with prayer, as he lifted his
eyes to the crucifix on the wall before him. After a few
seconds, he turned to Doña Ana. "I will do as you wish,
señora. Only permit me to call my Brothers so that I may
tell them what is to be done in my absence."

After Doña Ana had left the cell, and before the Brothers
gathered, John said to Anthony, "Nothing but obedience
to the Archbishop's command could induce me to make
such a sacrifice. I had hoped to end my days among my
Brothers and my poor. But since God wishes me to die
without that consolation, His will be done."

John stirred, lifted himself without help and stood a
moment in the pale rose and gilt light that filled the
austerely simple cell. He was an image carved in ivory,
clothed in the tunic that caught the last fire of the sun. A
slim, weightless hand touched Anthony's bowed head. The
grieving Brother looked up. John was smiling at him.
"You will succeed me, Anthony. Rely solely upon God's
goodness. You need no other help. There will be times
when you will find yourself at a loss what to do, where
to turn. In your needs on earth, turn to God, as you hope
one day to go to Him in Heaven. His purpose, His strength
will drive you on. The sick, the needy, the helpless are

His gifts to us. Cherish them." He waited. Then, trying for lightness, he continued, "Finding myself suddenly with nothing to do, after a life of work, is a little upsetting. Until God led me to Granada, I was constantly going here, going there. I had to learn to grow settled in restlessness. I was years and years waiting. Now—" he smiled—"I must wait again. I will be glad when the waiting is over."

Firm of step, John walked over to the window. The sunset sky of the late February day was a painter's palette daubed and streaked with gold, green and muted lavender-blues, shot through with the orange-vermillion of pomegranate flowers.

Watching him, Anthony felt faint with loss, as though John of God already had left this earth, and, in a sense, he had for he had surrendered to the inevitable. Anthony thought: Then he does know. He knows with absolute certainty that he never again will return to this cell or look upon the sky from that window. He knows, too, when he will die—apparently, very soon. He accepts it without fear; he has accepted with sublime obedience this final sacrifice which God demands of him. Still, his heart is breaking.

As though he read Anthony's thought, John said, without turning to him, "God is our Father. He does not inflict pain upon us without reason. If we cannot understand the reason, we know at least that grief draws us closer to Him, and that is what He wishes. Partings," he said meditatively, "I have known partings since I was nine years old. Soon I will go where there will be no partings any longer. Anthony—"

"Yes, Father—"

"Remain obedient. Offer obedience as you offer prayer.

Forget yourself, your feelings. Follow the judgment of the
Archbishop in all things, obey with your heart as well as
your lips. That is all."

His own words brought calm and courage to John himself, and there was again about him that holy glow that his
martyred flesh gave forth and which burned in his eyes.
A soul covered with the flame that was charity, that was
John of God. And this flame was to light his way into
eternity.

# TWENTY
# SEVEN

IN the afternoon, which was the afternoon of the seventh of March, Don Pedro de Guerrero, who had said Mass that morning at the altar which was set up in John's room, returned to visit him. Stretching out his episcopal hand, he felt the sick man's forehead.

"I am not feverish, Excellency. Do not call the doctor."

"If you are not feverish now, you must have been in a delirium of fever to do what you did shortly after midday. They told me, John." The Archbishop thanked the nobleman who had drawn a chair up for him beside the bed. "No wonder they have to post a gentleman in your room," he said to John. "The worry you gave us!"

"I know, Excellency. I shan't again." He hesitated. "But he gave me even greater worry."

"Who was he, John?"

"A poor weaver with a wife and children."

"Who told you about him?"

"No one, Excellency. Call it a revelation. I cannot explain it. I saw this man as in a dream. He was in a field, standing under a glitteringly green tree, a tree that stood out from all the others. From a jutting branch hung the rope with which he intended to hang himself. Was I to lie here and let him strangle himself into eternal punishment? He was about to take his life because he hadn't the means to support his family. I promised to recommend his needs to friends who would assist him. Then I came right back and went to bed again."

"Well, God be thanked for that."

"God be thanked," said John, "for giving me the strength to go to him. I am happy that I was able to deliver him from death, but I am happier still to know that mine is near. I wish only—" John stopped, did not say what he wished.

"You may have whatever you wish," Don Pedro assured him. His kindly eyes searched John's piercingly black ones for the unexpressed desire. He sensed uneasiness and hesitation in the dying man. Looking down at the veined, almost transparent hand on the silken bed cover, he impulsively pressed his fingers over it. "Something distresses you. As far as I am able, I would like to give you perfect peace of mind. Come now, tell me, what is it?"

"Three things trouble me, Excellency. I have been negligent, even cowardly, in my service to God. I leave this life without being able to pledge assistance to the poor in my hospital and to the families who have looked to me for help. What will happen to them? There is another thing, too. This morning Anthony brought to me a list of our debts. I was obliged to incur them, but I cannot pay them."

There was no reproach in the Archbishop, but only understanding and fondness. "John, none of us serves and loves God as well and as much as he ought. All your life you have relied upon His help; trust now in His mercy. By the merits of His Passion He will supply for all your weaknesses and faults. As for the poor, do not be uneasy. I adopt them as my children and will see to their needs. I would have done this in any case. It is my duty to support them.

And I give you my word that your creditors will be paid.
I myself will pay them. Now, let nothing disturb you.
Think only of the moment that will put an end to your
conflicts and sufferings. Pray for me, John of God, and
know that I will keep the promises which I have made you."

"Yes, yes," said John softly, and lay very still, his eyes
closed. He was smiling faintly, still hearing the words
promising help and comfort for his poor. "I am so grateful
to you, Excellency. I am so thankful that you came once
more to see me." Then he opened his eyes, and the two
friends looked at each other in a long, understanding
silence. Then John turned and gazed adoringly at the
crucifix on the altar before him.

I must go, Don Pedro thought. But he found it hard to
leave. He stood. "Is there anything else you wish?" he
asked in a low tone.

"No, Excellency." John did not look at him, nor pause
in his adoration of Christ on the Cross.

"Would you like to speak again to your Brothers?"

John's pale lips barely moved. He shook his head. Earlier in the day, they had been called to his bedside. He had
spoken with each one alone, and then he had given his last
counsel to them in a body. They were to be more faithful
in performing their duties than he had been, they were
to love the poor tenderly, to regard them as their masters
and themselves as the servants of the poor.

The Archbishop moved toward the door. About to open
it, he paused, looked at him again. John had not moved.
He seemed unaware of his presence. The room was quiet,
so quiet that John seemed already to have left it, consumed in the flame of his fervor. The face, with its deep
hollows and great, shining black eyes, was bathed in a
strange radiance. The Archbishop felt hot drops running

down his cheeks. Still in a trance of grief, he opened the door and left the room.

The hour wore away and another and yet another.

"Should we send for the doctor?" a servant asked, as Doña Ana came from the sickroom.

"I don't think the doctor is needed. Father John seems remarkably better. He asked me to read to him the Passion according to Saint John. He said that he wished to learn from Our Lord how to suffer. But the reading had quite the opposite effect."

"What do mean, señora?" asked one of several priests who were gathered outside the door of the room.

"The reading of the Passion appeared to remove all signs of suffering. Instead, it kindled his zeal. His pale and tired face became curiously youthful and animated. He had once again the vigor that one associates with him. Then, when I had come to the end, he asked to be left alone. He said he wished to rest."

The priest said: "Do you think he will really sleep?"

"He may. After a day of seeing so many people, he ought to be exhausted. And it is already late."

Later yet, moonlight and the light of a vigil lamp mingled together and illumined the Son of God nailed to the cross which stood on the altar in John's room. In the patio, palm trees rustled in the night wind. The clash of frond on frond awakened John. His eyes went immediately to the moonlit crucifix. Something began to thrill and quiver in him. His heart was beating so fast that he thought he would faint. He let himself lie back on his pillows, but only for a moment. The hour had come. He threw aside the covers, got up, put on his habit, closed his fingers around his crucifix and sank to his knees before the altar, saying in a clear, exalted voice, "Jesus, Jesus, into Thy hands I commend my spirit."

At the same instant the room seemed to be visited by a number of persons going in and then out of it. Doña Ana, a few of her close friends, wives of the noblemen who were in the corridor, and the several priests heard these mysterious sounds, but as the footsteps faded almost as suddenly as they had come, those outside the room told themselves it was delusion.

"What time is it?" said Don Juan de Guevaro.

"A few minutes after midnight."

One of the priests approached the door. He stood there listening. No sound came from within. He murmured to Doña Ana, "Señora, I do not like this. It is too quiet in there. His sleep is too long for one who never sleeps and who is so ill. I am going in." He opened the door, sighed with relief. "He is on his knees before the altar. The reading of the Passion must indeed have had a miraculous effect upon him. Let us not disturb him." Very carefully he closed the door. But another priest who had caught a glimpse of the kneeling figure shook his head. "He is as still as stone," he said, and eyed the door with a little fear. "Open it, please, Father."

When they went up to John he did not stir.

"John of God," said the priest, gently, bending over him.

He did not speak or move. There was a smile of grave sweetness upon his lips. His face had paled to marble whiteness.

"Is he in ecstasy? You call out his name," said the one priest to the other.

"John of God. Brother Zero."

The two priests waited anxiously.

There was no reply, no motion, no lifting of the long, dark lashes that lay upon his cheeks like fine brush strokes

of shadow. The only answer was an indescribable fragrance that filled the room. It was as if the cool March wind had blown into it the soft perfume of a whole field of mingled flowers.

When had he died? Sometime between the last breath of Friday and the first of Saturday, the one being the day on which Christ had died and the other the day which the Church consecrates to the honor of the Blessed Virgin Mary. It was the eighth of March, in the year 1550, his fifty-fifth birthday. And, as at the time of his birth, the miracle which took place on that eighth of March in Montemor-o-Novo now was repeated in Granada. All the churchbells rang without being touched by human hands. On and on the tolling bells dropped a pall of mournful sound over the ancient city which God had destined to be the cross of John of God. It was his glory as well. For there he attained sanctity through annihilation of self in God. The little cipher, the zero mark, his symbol of nothingness, became his halo.

# NOTE

DURING his lifetime, John of God gave no formal Rule to his followers. His own virtues set the example which they faithfully imitated. Six years after his death the Rule which bears his name was written and decreed. Pope St. Pius V gave canonical approval to the Order of Charity in a papal Bull of January 1, 1571. In this Bull he imposed upon the members of this Order the obligation to follow the Rule of St. Augustine. He also stated the form of the habit to be worn, adding to the original tunic and cincture the scapular and hooded cowl, and authorized the members to take Holy Orders. Four vows are observed: Poverty, Chastity, Obedience and Hospitality.

Pope Urban VIII declared John of God beatified in 1630, and in 1690 Pope Alexander VIII canonized him. In 1886, Pope Leo XIII declared Saint John of God the patron Saint of hospitals and the sick, with Saint Camillus de Lellis, and in 1930 Pope Pius XI named Saint John of God the heavenly patron of nurses.

# SELECTED BIBLIOGRAPHY

Allbutt, T. C. *Historical Relations of Medicine and Surgery, To the End of the Sixteenth Century:* Macmillan, New York, 1905.

Atkinson, D. T., M.D. *Magic, Myth and Medicine:* World Publishing Co., New York, 1956.

Blunt, Hugh F. *Great Penitents:* Macmillan, New York, 1922.

Bollandists. *Chap. LV, No. 19. Chap. XLV., Nos. 22-23.*

Brown, E. G. *Arabian Medicine:* Macmillan, New York, 1921.

*Bullarium Romanum. Vol. XX:* Naples, 1883.

Capilla, Antonio Alarcón. *La Granada de Oro.* Madrid, Pablo Lopez, 1950.

Castro, Francisco de. *Miraculosa Vida y santos Obras del Beato Juan de Dios:* Granada, 1588.

Clavijo y Clavijo, Salvador. *Breve Historia de la Orden Hospitalaria,* etc: Madrid, Artes Gráficas ARGES, 1950.

Clavijo y Clavijo, Salvador. *La Orden Hospitalaria de S. Juan de Dios en la Marina de Guerra de España* etc.: Madrid, Tipografia Artistica, 1950.

*Comissão Nacional Para as Comemorações do IV Centenario de São João de Deus:* Lisbon, 1950.

Currier, C. W. *History of Religious Orders:* New York, 1894.

Dios, San Juan de. *Cartas y Escritas de N.G.P. San Juan de Dios:* Madrid, 1935.

Fabro, Cornelio. *Colloqui su S. Giovanni di Dio:* Rome, Ecclesia, No. 7. July, 1948.

Figueras, Sebastian Montserrat. *Las Actividades Medico-Castrenses de la Inclita Orden Hospitalaria de S. Juan de Dios:* Madrid, Julio Soto, 1950.

Garrison, Fielding H. *Introduction to the History of Medicine:* W. B. Saunders Co., Philadelphia, 1913.

Garrison, Fielding H. *Bulletin of the New York Academy of Medicine.* Vol. VII. No. 8. August, 1931.

Gasquet, Dom Francis Aiden, O.S.B. *Preface to Letters of Bl. John of Avila:* Burns & Oates, London, 1904.

Giordani, Igino. *Giovanni di Dio, Santo del Populo; Casa Editrice Adriano Salani:* Florence, 1947.

Gomez-Moreno, Manuel. *Primicias Historicas de San Juan de Dios:*

Madrid, S. Aguirre, 1950.

Goodier, Alban. *Saints for Sinners:* Longmans, Green & Co., New York, 1938.

Goodier, Alban. *Saints Are Not Sad:* New York, 1949.

Granada, Luis de. *Vida del Ven. Maestro Juan de Avila:* Madrid, 1787.

Grassi, Galdino, O. H. *San Giovanni di Dio:* Rome, 1887.

Labrador, Antonio. *Vida del Padre de los Pobres:* Madrid, 1947.

Lambert, S. W. & Goodwin, G. M. *Medical Leaders from Hippocrates to Osler:* Bobbs-Merrill Co., Indianapolis, 1929.

Les Petits Bollandistes. *Vie des Saints.* Vol. VIII. Paris, 1888.

Loyac, Jean de. *Le Triomphe de la Charité en la vie de S. Jean de Dieu. Blanc & Bernard,* Marseille, 1883.

Magnin, Ignace Marie. *Hero of Charity. Alexander Ouseley, Ltd.,* Westminster, S.W., 1935.

Magnin, Ignace Marie. *Vie de S. Jean de Dieu. A. Taffin-Lefort,* Paris, 1887.

McMahon, Norbert. *St. John of God.* New York, *McMullen,* 1953.

Meyer, Raphael. *Vie de S. Jean de Dieu:* 1897.

Paz y Caridad. *Album Commemorativo* etc. *Segunda Parte.* No. 6. Nov.–Dec., Madrid, 1950.

Peers, E. Allison. *Study of the Spanish Mystics.* Vol. 11. Sheldon Press, London, 1927.

Pinto, Rodrigo Gonzales, M.D. *La Obra Hospitalaria en la Asistencia a Las Enfermos Mentales:* Madrid, Artes Gráficas ARGES, 1950.

Pozo, Luciano del. *Vida de San Juan de Dios:* Madrid, 1929.

Roy, R. *Beloved Soldier of Portugal:* (Ave Maria. No. 72. August, 1950).

Russotto, P. Gabriele. *La Sigla di S. Giovanni di Dio:* (Vita Ospedaliera. March, 1957).

Saglier, L'Abbe L. *Vie de S. Jean de Dieu. E. Plon & Cie.:* Paris, 1877.

Speakman, Elizabeth. *Medieval Hospitals.* (The Dublin Review. Vol. 133. Art. V. October, 1903).

Sudhoff, Karl. *Essays on the History of Medicine:* Medical File Press, New York, 1926.

Trapadoux, Marc. *Histoire de S. Jean de Dieu.*

Villethierri, Girard de. *Vie de S. Jean de Dieu:* Paris, 1691.

Walsh, James J. *Medieval Medicine:* Macmillan, New York, 1920.

was born in San Antonio, Texas. She holds the degrees of Bachelor and Master of Arts in English. Small and soft-spoken, she is a hard worker and writes best in small quarters suited to her size. She is her own severest critic. Out of every 500 pages of typed manuscript, she burns 490. Her books include a curious assortment of subjects—a Negro emperor, two Cardinals, the author of *Don Quixote,* the conqueror of Mexico, the patron saint of hospitals, an English artist, an American School Sister, a horse and a coatimundi. She is married to artist-author Addison Burbank, who has illustrated most of her books.